Benchmarking

for

Continuous

Improvement

in the

Public

Sector

by
Dr John R N Bullivant

Benchmarking for Continuous Improvement in the Public Sector

Published by Longman Information & Reference
Longman Group Limited, Westgate House, The High, Harlow,
Essex CM20 1YR, United Kingdom.
Telephone: (0279) 442601
Facsimile: (0279) 444501

First published 1994

A catalogue record for this book is available from the British Library.

ISBN 0-582-24434-X

Typeset in 11/12pt Sabon

Printed and bound in Great Britain by Bookcraft (Bath) Ltd.

Dedication

This book is dedicated to Bev and young Jack, the 'best of the best'.

I would also like to thank all the staff at NHS Wales VFM Unit and the NHS Benchmarking Reference Centre for all their hard work and support.

John Bullivant
Wrexham
May 1994

Contents

Foreword

'The NHS in Wales is proud of its tradition of innovation in new services, in clinical techniques and in organisational development. We have a reputation for developing new approaches and strategies and for comparing and sharing these with colleagues elsewhere.

Our commitment to improving the health of the people of Wales is well documented and we are matching that commitment with a drive to improve the quality of services to meet the needs and wishes of patients.

We must always remember that the simple reason for all our work is to improve the health and care of people in our communities. This requires us to know what we are doing and how well. It requires us to ask public and patients what they think of our services and to respond to their concerns and aspirations. I know many of our colleagues in Industry have learnt this lesson and some have used benchmarking as the means to success.

I am particularly pleased therefore that in Wales we have now taken a lead with the benchmarking initiative as I know this offers a valuable method for translating our strategies and commitments into action.'

John Wyn Owen
Director NHS Wales
introducing the second
NHS Benchmarking Conference
on World Quality Day (11.11.93)

John Wyn Owen, CB, is now Director General, Health Department New South Wales

while it is very innovative, and is now much more focused on patient's needs and cost-effective use of resources, it is an extremely complex organisation and still very inefficient in learning the lessons, both successes and failures of others. Reinventing the wheel is a popular pastime, but with limited resources it is a luxury we cannot afford. Benchmarking can help to achieve improvements in quality, productivity and cost management and I would like to see the approach used as the driver for continual improvement. My target audience is those who have a commitment to improve constantly and continuously and my first objective is that your commitment to be the best is supported by an approach which finds that wheel before you have to reinvent it.

Two, I recognise that the management agenda in the NHS and in many other public services is enormous. Few industries face the complexity of services, partnerships, regulation, scrutiny and political pressures that we do. Benchmarking can help to focus attention on the important issues and make a real impact. However there is a danger in constant change which is not based upon an understanding of the values and approach currently practised. My second objective is that you are convinced of the value of benchmarking so you give up some of your valuable time to know your organisation before you seek to change it.

Three, I think we are in danger of forgetting the motivations of staff in public sector organisations. We may undermine the best of public service with the worst of market forces. Benchmarking relies more on pride and commitment in providing the best than in slapping wrists over poor performance in league tables. This is not to say we cannot learn from commercial managers. 'It is the same attitude which gives top class quality and top class value – an obsessive wish to do things better' (Griffiths R, 1991). Benchmarking can provide the stimulus and method for managers and staff to recognise best in class status using process mapping and performance measurement. But we also need the humility and generosity to be prepared to learn and share with others. My third objective is that you understand the value and method of learning from the best, whoever they may be.

The Approach in this Book

I have tried to practice what I preach and therefore gave some thought to the style and layout of the book and what I was trying to achieve.

I recalled that ICL had told me that when redesigning their computer system instruction manuals they had looked about for a style that effectively conveyed technical information to an informed but non-technical audience, ie to a do-it-yourself audience. They recognised that car repair manuals were effective and successful and began to emulate those books.

You will find the approach is therefore similar to the DIY guides available for cooking, gardening and house repairs. Table 1 in the next chapter will help you to identify how prepared your organisation is for benchmarking, whilst Table 2 illustrates common problems and their solution.

How to Use the Book

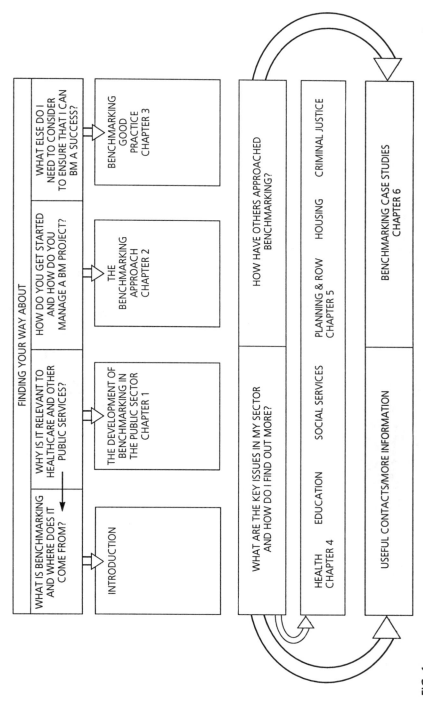

FIG. 1

Unresolvable by Other Means

Benchmarking can help to clarify the issues, but is an extravagant way of confirming that unfinished business is still unfinished. Many issues can be resolved simply by giving them attention or following through on difficult decisions. Others may need the benefit of the attention of a multi-disciplinary team to aid both issue resolution and broad commitment. Benchmarking is really for those key issues where the problem is identified but the solution is not clear.

What are the Keys to Successful Benchmarking?

The approach relies on commitment and application. This means understanding where the organisation stands now by mapping the process and measuring performance, seeking out high performers and securing their support. Finally it means effective project management to implement the necessary changes.

Commitment

It is essential that the programme has senior management commitment to be successful. The programme relates most successfully to key business issues and these should therefore be owned by those leading the organisation. Senior managers tend to value the approach because it tackles issues of concern to them but also because it deals with the detail of service delivery or internal operation which is something they are far removed from and of which they have little understanding.

Process Mapping

This is an old skill used by many disciplines to graphically represent the chronological sequence of activity. The approach highlights process ownership (ie which department or group does what) and the distinction between value added and value lost activity. This approach combined with process measurement supports significant improvements through re-engineering.

Process Measurement

Measurement of inputs, outputs and outcomes are all possible. Too often measurement systems record that which is easy to record, eg the ordering of service or the days spent on it, rather than the delivery of service or completion to target within budget.

Few internal processes are measured and system failures whilst obvious may disguise the cause behind a presenting problem. Process mapping helps to identify key problem areas, ownership of process and preferred measurement points.

The development of meaningful high level or core indicators requires clear definition, explicit rationale, unambiguous formula and validation of usefulness and cost of collection.

Identification of High Performers

Having identified process problems and poor relative performance, benchmarking partners need to be identified. These are the organisations who achieve best in class status for the activity or process under investigation. The best performer may be a world leader in the process because this is their core business, whereas for the NHS for example it is only a supporting activity. It may be that they have a completely different purpose, organisation and cultural or payment systems but if the process is the same and they are better at it, we can learn from them.

Goodwill from Benchmarking Partners

Generally the public sector benefits from goodwill in supporting our work from all sectors. Following the guidance on 'code of conduct' and 'benchmarking visits' will assist in establishing an etiquette which builds and maintains that goodwill. The code also helps organisations who may naturally be your competitor to recognise those areas where mutual benefit can be achieved by sharing performance and experience even if some areas are closed to discussion.

Effective Project Management

Much of benchmarking is simply related to effective project management. Clarity of purpose, timetable, deliverables and roles will ensure the work is undertaken and benefits realised. However the benchmarking approach emphasises the value of preparatory work undertaken before seeking to implement change.

This approach can be more systematically presented as the 12 steps to successful benchmarking which are adapted from those established by Rank Xerox Camp RC, 1989 (Fig. 2).

Plan

Step 1. Select Subject Area

Step 2. Define Process to Benchmark

Step 3. Identify Potential Benchmarking Partners

Step 4. Identify Data Required

Analysis

Step 5. Collect the Data and Select Benchmark Partners

Step 6. Determine the Gap Compared to Benchmark

Step 7. Establish Difference in Process

Step 8. Target Future Performance

Action

Step 9. Communication and Commitment

Step 10. Adjust Targets and Develop Corrective Improvement Plan

Step 11. Implementation and Monitoring

Step 12. Review Progress and Recalibrate

FIG. 2   The 12 Steps to Successful Benchmarking

What is the Relevance of Benchmarking to the Public Sector?

Benchmarking in the public sector is about people. It is about providing the best services possible with least overheads and least delay. It is achieved by close examination of current services and comparison and learning from those who have already achieved success.

In the hospital it is about getting the patient to the best treatment as quickly as possible, providing that treatment on the basis of knowing that it works, and then getting the patient home or on to appropriate care as quickly as possible, consistent with their needs. It is about staff in the hospital and outside working together to achieve that care for patients, so for example it is about getting the patient, surgeon, anaesthetist, nurses and medical records to the theatre at the same time and it is about 'creating' the department for getting people home rather than ward nurse, medical records, pharmacy and ambulance service all thinking it is not their fault if you stay in hospital another few hours or another night after being discharged by the consultant.

Benchmarking requires comparative performance indicators but it is not simply about your position on league tables. The need for this information is firstly to indicate that better performance is achievable and secondly to give guidance on who to talk to to find out how they achieved their success.

The motivation for benchmarking in the public sector is not simply for competitive advantage, rather it is to support two traditional but important values, pride in your work and that of your organisation and the vocation commitment of providing a public service and providing it well.

Seeking to be the 'best of the best' may be tautological and improbable but it is not an idle slogan; it is appropriate because it is inspiring and because it recognises the continous journey involved in providing services that can always be improved.

The public authority has changed and in some cases disappeared in the traditional sense of providing services. In some areas it may seem that all the statutory authorities have been replaced by quangos, voluntary organisations and private providers. For this reason in considering current opportunities for improvement when quoting examples I have tried to use a variety of organisations now intrinsically involved in determining need, providing services and monitoring their effectiveness. These include NHS Trusts, commercial schools inspectors, non-profit making housing associations, voluntary groups and traditional local government organisations.

This strong policy change on the organisation of public services should lead to a more consistent approach and level of performance but the Audit Commission reports highlight a continuing degree of variance in provision and access to public services which continues to confirm Kogan's belief that only 'the range and level, but not the style and quality of local authorities activities are prescribed by central government.' (Kogan M, 1971 p 27).

Benchmarking has a particular value in public service. Not only is the public sector subjected to increasing pressure to be business like, to be competitive and to demonstrate value for money but the services are expected to demonstrate equity and probity all under the critical gaze of staff, users, auditors, the press, politicians and public account committees. The criteria for assessing public services in NHS Wales annual reviews have been listed (after Maxwell R J, 1984 p 1470) as:

A. effectiveness – for individual patients and the population as a whole;

B. equity – equal treatment for equal need;

C. access to services – in terms of location and waiting times, and so on;

D. relevance to need – for the whole community and appropriate care for the individual;

E. social acceptability – including responsiveness to the views of patients and their families and friends; and

F. efficiency – value for money.

Both the public and the Audit Commission have difficulty in understanding why large variations in services occur in different locations. The obvious conclusion would seem to be to learn from the best.

Benchmarking through process mapping helps to identify where practice has deviated from policy or guidelines. Many public services (council housing, hospital operations, schools admissions) are still rationed by queues and available places. It is true that many consumers are still like the miner in Orwell's *Road to Wigan Pier* (1937) only conscious of the problem when told about it, but this is often because those who enjoy quicker access to services are not about to cry foul. A system which is inequitable by design or default is difficult to justify.

This may have been acceptable in the 1970s for example when schools described different methods in use from those the local authority said it was practising (Potter G R, 1970) and 'the basis for selection was not merit, but the knowledge of the system' (Bullivant J, 1981) but it fails to meet the public's expectations in the 1990s.

What is the History of Benchmarking

Watson (1993) has outlined the development of benchmarking in the USA as consisting of five phases:

Phase 1	1950–1975	Reverse engineering
Phase 2	1976–1986	Competitive benchmarking
Phase 3	1982–1988	Process benchmarking
Phase 4	1988+	Strategic benchmarking
Phase 5	1993+	Global benchmarking.

The first phase was one of *reverse engineering* or stripping down a product, eg a car gearbox, and to find technical improvements which could be 'copied'. The origins of this are unknown but must go back to the first individual who did not insist on re-inventing the wheel.

After 1976 the second phase of *competive benchmarking* was largely associated with Rank Xerox's need to dramatically improve cost management in the face of Japanese competition. This phase examined the processes of manufacturing and delivering the product as well as the technical merits of the product itself. Rank Xerox used its subsidiary Fuji Xerox to assist in this process.

Watson argues a third phase ran from 1976 to 1986 when companies realised it was easier to learn from organisations with whom they were not in competition. This *process benchmarking* required some lateral thinking in searching out best in class performers from unrelated industry. The classic example is Xerox learning from the LL Bean mail order firm (Camp R C, 1989 p 103). A health example would be to learn about theatre scheduling from an airline scheduler.

The fourth phase is *strategic benchmarking* where the intent is to fundamentally change the business not just the process. Re-engineering will result more quickly and effectively through benchmarking with organisations already in the new field. Usually this will require some form of alliance from which both organisations perceive benefits.

Global benchmarking seeks to remove all extraneous factors by first understanding them and recognising the contribution they make. In health this would be the recognition that although health-care is organised and financed in many different ways, fundamentally the activity is the same. For example we can therefore learn much from health-care overseas, regardless AND because of different funding and rationing mechanisms.

How is Benchmarking Progressing in the UK?

The DTI sees benchmarking as a TQM tool and in 1992 reprinted the Booklet *Best Practice Benchmarking* which was originally issued in 1989 as part of the managing into the 1990s programme.

The first interest was shown by insurance companies and US offshoots such as Digital, Milliken and Rank Xerox, but they were rapidly followed by UK/European organisations such as British Steel, British Telecom, ICI, Shell and Rover. A benchmarking seminar was organised in 1991 by the British Quality Association and this was quickly followed by a number of major conferences. In April 1992 the European Foundation for Quality Management supported the A T Kearney/Qmas conference for competitive advantage in Birmingham. This included the Bob Camp workshop and presentations from British Steel, Rover, TNT and British Airways as well as contributions from Digital and Corning.

Attending the conference were over 230 delegates including delegates from the Department of Social Security, Department of Employment and NHS Wales (Status Meetings, 1992).

The conference was organised by Status Meetings Ltd who recognising the interest in benchmarking then went on to establish an all industry Benchmarking Centre Ltd.

In 1993 a survey on benchmarking was carried out by Gallup on behalf of Coopers and Lybrand and the Confederation of British Industry's National Manufacturing Council (CBI, 1993).

The survey found that 67% of respondents claimed they were currently undertaking some form of benchmarking. Although two-thirds had only started formal benchmarking in the last five years, 72% said they compared their performance in quantitative terms and their processes with others. Ninety per cent of companies believed they had benefited from undertaking benchmarking and were positive about the approach.

There is some scepticism about the results and the extent to which detailed benchmarking is really being undertaken but there is undeniably an interest in the approach. In 1993 several studies appeared extolling the virtues of the approach, for example the Cardiff Business School led 'Lean Enterprise Benchmarking Project' in automotive component companies in the UK and Japan concluded that 'benchmarking is the most powerful tool for assessing industrial competitiveness and for triggering the change process in companies striving for world class performance' (Andersen Consulting, 1993). Perhaps more importantly to public sector organisations an increasing awareness of the value and methods of sharing information was to be seen.

What is the Difference Between Benchmarking, Quality and TQM?

There is often confusion as to the relationship between benchmarking and TQM, and the relationship of both to Quality.

Is Benchmarking Simply a Repackaging of Old Ideas?

There is in practice little that is new in benchmarking; you may find most of the techniques involved are familiar but there are strong themes of pareto, value for money, customer focus, empowerment and benchmarking of the benchmarking approach which combine to make this a powerful support to managing and surviving change.

Benchmarking is usually presented as part of the toolkit of a quality approach. It can be viewed more as a style of working.

You may use benchmarking as means of continual improvement or in time you can adopt the principal of continual improvement through benchmarking as the normal way of working. Benchmarking supports the management of change, but as we increasingly realise that change is itself the norm, benchmarking provides a means of flowing with change, and responding to change by managing our response.

The Mississippi floods of 1993 brought into question whether a hundred years of river engineering was the right way to control the river. The constant changes in the river, the enormous expense of maintaining the earthworks and the catastrophic impact of unpredicted floods suggested a need to work with the river, rather than against it and to manage our use of the river rather than manage or control the river itself.

What is Quality?

Quality is difficult to understand. Is it a noun, an absolute, a state to achieve, eg that suit has 'quality', or is it an adjective relative to other things or services, eg 'that is a quality shoeshine' meaning better than another one. Is quality synonomous with good, best or excellence or does it mean fit for task and safe to use. What does best quality or poor quality mean? Can you buy middle quality apples? If you could, would that mean some good and bad or all intermediate. Is the term meaningful any more?

Indeed Pirsig (1991) argues that 'quality isn't definable' that 'quality is value', ie that like beauty or art the concept is dependent on the eye of the beholder. Similarly Per Dalin describes a good school as one which has come to terms with itself, its organisation and its participants but also has values with which we individually identify. 'A "good" school is a school that is good for "me".' (Dalin P, 1978 p 54).

The *Concise Oxford Dictionary* (1990) defines 'quality as the degree of excellence of a thing' but then defines excellence as 'surpassing quality'. Pirsig sidesteps the issue by suggesting the metaphysics of quality is analogous to the high country of mountain climbing. 'It takes a lot of effort to get there and more effort when you arrive, but unless you can make the journey you are confined to one valley of thought all your life' (Pirsig, 1991 flyleaf).

Quality is easier to understand when there is some standard to relate it to. The early history of quality efforts started with detection to weed out the defects, through a process of quality control by comparing products produced with an ideal specification through measuring and testing to eliminate the cause of the problem, to the system of quality assurance which seeks to avoid problems by planning, design and documentation of systems to avoid the problems arising in the first place. To provide some consistency and support a number of standard setting (eg ANSI-ASQC Q90/BS5750/ISO 9000) and accreditation systems have been developed.

BS5750

BS5750 is an audit of quality management processes with origins in the USA as an attempt to control high rates of malfunction in military equipment in the Second World War.

Its present form was established in 1979.

'The BS5750 series are the national standards which promulgate, for use by UK suppliers and purchasers, the ISO 9000 series international standards for quality systems.' (DTI, 1987 p4.)

'BS5750 sets out how you can establish, document and maintain an effective quality system which will demonstrate to your customers that you are committed to quality and are able to supply their quality needs.' (DTI, 1987 p7.)

It is a useful first step on the quality journey but few organisations use it in its intended context as a first step towards total quality management.

Intended to provide quality consistency, it is often pursued because large firms demand certification for major suppliers.

It charts existing procedures, but if there are inefficient, all an organisation is doing is locking in their inefficiencies. The process offers consistency but not necessarily improvement.

The process of adopting BS5750 can therefore be an expensive way of institutionalising the status quo.

Recently local councils were advised it would be wrong to demand BS5750 accreditation in competitive tendering arrangements.

The focus of quality efforts has moved from the end of the line through the production process to the setting-up stage. Inherent in these efforts is that quality does not just happen by itself, it needs to be managed. However there is a weakness in these approaches. All of them infer that quality is the responsibility of the checker, the Quality Control Department, the Quality Assurance Manager or the accreditation team. If they don't plan or check everything, quality will escape and defects re-emerge (see however Housing Quality Initiation in Ch 5).

What is TQM?

The current answer to the problem of ownership of quality in the organisation is seen as Total Quality Management (TQM). TQM is a concept which embraces the whole organisation, not just the manufacture of the product but also design, delivery, billing and service. TQM is a commitment to a company-wide culture where everyone is clear of the direction and objectives of the organisation and work in support of each other to achieve these goals. The approach is usually heavily focused on customer satisfaction and continuous improvement. However there is no blueprint for TQM and organisations must create their own approach to TQM perhaps by learning from others and by selecting from the wide range of quality and management practices and tools.

Common TQM Principles
  Customer satisfaction
  Employee involvement
  Right First Time
  Continuous improvement
  Commitment to organisational goals
  Continual improvement
  Supportive leadership
  Ownership and empowerment.

Common TQM Practices and Skills
  Communications
  Problem solving
  Decision making and taking
  Statistical methods
  Business process analysis
  Modelling
  Project planning
  Documentation
  Cross functional teams
  Benchmarking.

TQM however is a management approach rather than a cultural belief and therefore needs commitment and effort to maintain momentum. It is a long haul approach and will flounder if too much is expected too soon. It is expensive and requires a lot of explaining and training.

John Oakland (1989) in his book *Total Quality Management* recognised that whilst TQM's time had arrived it would not survive unless its supporters were realistic in their claims. He and others have identified problems emerging such as:

Managers losing commitment and reverting to short-term gains

Lack of organisational focus on quality leading to scepticism

TQM being written off as last year's management agenda

Teams becoming bogged down in trivia instead of tackling important problems

Organisations producing quality plans but no action

Managers and staff confusing attendance on training courses with establishing a quality organisation

Effort concentrating on the cosmetic trappings of new logos and uniforms

Quality success being measured by the achievement of quality standard certificates and awards rather than customer satisfaction.

Quality initiatives in many public sector organisations demonstrate these failings. As Chief executives seek to deal with cash limits and public relations disasters, they can lose interest in long term strategies. The efforts sink rather than cascade down the organisation as 'Quality Managers' struggle to maintain enthusiasm and resources. Quality becomes an end in itself rather than the means to customer satisfaction and business survival.

How Does Marketing Link to TQM and Benchmarking?

In the health service quality was briefly overtaken by a new concept 'marketing'. This seemed to contain all the elements of TQM but with a stronger concentration on the customer as king. This concept is complicated in public services provided free at the point of delivery as providers of services inevitably have to focus on the surrogate purchasers of services (eg health authorities and fundholding GPs) as well as the actual consumers or users (eg patients). Internally each part of the organisation can be seen as having internal customers for example the pathology department provides services to clinical departments, the porters provide a service to the pathology department, the catering department provides services to porters etc.

Marketing however is a business process which has the wrong image in public services and is yet to become universally acceptable. The concept of the internal market in health is still under scrutiny and 'marketing' still sounds too much like the selling of public services than the focusing of resources to meet the needs of patients that it could be. No doubt its time will come but as yet it is still a Cinderella activity. (Hawley and Ferguson, 1992.)

Where Does the Quality Movement Stand Now?

It is probably in need of some revitalisation and refocusing. The concept of quality as a good thing still stands but is balanced with the need to demonstrate value for money spent. It may be true that quality failures cost, but so do quality improvement failures.

New approaches need to be more pragmatic and less evangelising. They need to be replicable and less dependent on charismatic visionaries.

Like Pirsig (1991) I conclude that I am sceptical of the value of the term 'quality', it is over-used and ambiguous. We need a new term to describe the state of services we aspire to provide. 'Healthy' is a term which suggests a desire to achieve a better state but recognises the term is relative not only to current health but changes in personal circumstances, eg age and the external environment.

The *Concise Oxford Dictionary* (1990) suggests healthy means 'having, showing and promoting good health'. Public services need to have good health (financial and organisational), to be seen to have good health (accountability) and to promote good health (continuous improvement). The rest of this book is about how to manage change by benchmarking for healthy services.

What is the Difference Between Cost Reduction, Re-engineering and Benchmarking?

Cost reduction is a constant feature of both public and commercial services. In the health service it has been formalised into the annual cost improvement targets. In industry it is usually represented by attention to cost control to offset the inflationary elements of materials, currencies or staff. The traditional approach relies on target setting and value for money studies but both of these approaches have faced difficulties, either because they have tackled the wrong issues or because the targets have been set too low or too high often based on simple extrapolation of the past.

Re-engineering is the systematic redesign and improvement of products. It usually involves a fundamental rethinking and redesigning of business processes or the business itself. The emphasis is on the need for dramatic internal change and reduction of costs because the traditional services or goods are no longer required or because of severe pressure or competition in the market place. Often the approach is associated with a rethink of the focus of the business, eg away from providing fast food towards filling stomachs. The NHS is going through a process of re-engineering with its attention shift to achieving health gain as opposed to providing hospital services. Within hospitals, the adoption of patient focused care where services are grouped around the patient rather than the patient travelling to the X-ray or physiotherapy department are examples of re-engineering.

The advocates of re-engineering are critical of traditional attempts at cost reduction or quality improvement describing these attempts as little more than 'sacking the dinner ladies' or 'moving the deckchairs around on the Titanic'. The distinction is therefore often presented as one of scale with cost/quality improvement activities aiming for modest 1% improvements and re-engineering projects seen as more catastrophic seeking to achieve wholesale refocusing.

Critics of re-engineering point to the expense of change, the social cost of large numbers of redundancies and the high failure rates in big bang approaches. In practice the picture is not as tidy as this and suggests the various approaches are still immature or poorly implemented. The cost improvement approach has improved recently with less 'fire-fighting' and more attention to identification and planning of schemes, to project management and benefit realisation and conversely re-engineering is beginning to be adopted in more modest areas of change.

How Does Cost Reduction and Re-engineering Relate to Benchmarking?

Benchmarking is an option in cost reduction, quality improvement and re-engineering. Benchmarking helps to identify key issues, how they operate now and the failure points that need improvement. Costing and time measurement of process elements assists in identifying the cost drivers (ie those elements that contribute significantly to total cost and cost variability) thereby focusing attention on areas where cost reduction can be achieved to most effect. Benchmarking can also assist in avoiding the disruption of wholesale re-engineering by demonstrating how seemingly intractable problems have been overcome by benchmarking against those who have been more successful. Patient focused care for example might be better achieved by resolving internal communications and transport of patients and services within the hospital rather than relocating staff and physical rebuilding. Benchmarking can also assist in how best to use these techniques. Johnson and Johnson, for example, have benchmarked with world class companies to see how they implement process re-engineering (J & J Hospital Services Inc, 1993).

How do I Know Where my Organisation Stands in Relation to Benchmarking?

Table 1 presents a maturity matrix of an organisations status

TABLE 1   Issue: Benchmarking

Elements	Pre take-off audit	Minimum level planning	Good practice partnership	Best practice maturity
Improvement focus	Developing capabilities/ process improvement	Internal	External	Customer satisfaction
Improvement players	Quality team	All staff	Network teams	Board & staff
Measures	Central returns/ League tables	BS5750 Accreditation	Awards opt-in measurement	Published performance
Relationships	Us and them	Internal customers	Cross functional. Commissioners. Suppliers	Pareto Corporate generous, individually selfish
Benchmarking	No	Flow charting. External Consultant surveys. 'Study to learn'	Key business processes functional	High value and opportunity widespread with confidence
Decision making based on	Top manager	Functional teams	Multifunctional teams	Information
Problems	Product	Complexity	Professional boundaries and language	Time management
Product design	Design team	Process owners	Consumer	Consumers, employees suppliers
Customer contact	Sales	Satisfaction surveys	Customer involved	Customer led

My Benchmarking Project is Failing, What is Going Wrong?

The DTI had already anticipated that some companies would find benchmarking difficult and produced a table of likely causes for failure points (Table 2).

TABLE 2

Problem	Likely causes	Solution
Benchmarking the wrong measure	Inadequate knowledge of own organisation and operations	Further research to find significant measures
Benchmarking the wrong organisation	Inadequate desk research	More detailed initial research
Benchmarking not leading to action	Senior management not involved	Ensure that management is seen to be in support
Failure to sell idea to senior management	Lack of information, poor presentation	Tie Best Practice Benchmarking firmly to the existing business plan; show how other companies have benefited
Lack of resources for benchmarking	Lack of management support; exclusive ownership by the Best Practice Benchmarking team	Lobby and promote Best Practice Benchmarking as a company-wide approach
Data not meaningful	Too much/too little data; data not comparable	Tighter focus on measures; test the assumption about your processes that generated the measures
Inaccurate/false data	Over-reliance on public or competitor sources	Double-check sources through personal checks
Failure to sell idea to target organisations	Scepticism and protective instincts	Make clear the benefits of shared information; reassess criteria for selection of partners
Over-reliance on superficial similarity with partner	Lack of rigorous criteria for assessing partners	Redefine search to find closer fits
Benchmarking partner unwillling to share useful data	Benchmark partner too alike	Define search by process not industry
Benchmark too many measures	Unclear priorities	Relate Best Practice Benchmarking to business plan

Source: *Best Practice Benchmarking* DTI, 1992.

Table 1 shows a maturity matrix for benchmarking. The use of such matrices is described in Chapter 3, but here a number of elements are highlighted with identifiable characteristics of an organisation before starting benchmarking; at the planning stage; in partnership with other organisations and reaching best practice maturity. This will help to identify the status and balance of benchmarking type activities already working in your organisation and to plan future activity (NHSBRC, 1994). Whereas Table 2 will help you to realise why your efforts have stalled and to apply corrective measures.

In Conclusion What is Benchmarking and What is it Not?

Benchmarking is:
  innovative
  pareto based
  customer focused
  success orientated
  comparison with the best
  an improvement process
  empowerment
  sharing and learning
  breakthrough thinking
  about implementation
  developing healthy services
  energising.

Benchmarking is not:
  new
  cost cutting
  just competitive analysis
  number crunching
  site tours
  just copying or catch-up
  spying or espionage
  lone ranger activity
  quick and easy
  stealing ideas
  concerned with average performance.

Chapter 1
The Development of Benchmarking in the Public Sector

This chapter reviews the recent changes in policy in the health service, the rebalance of attention towards improving the health of the community rather than simply providing health-care and how this move is being supported by the parallel efforts to develop cost effectiveness and quality in the provision of services. The chapter then rehearses in detail the introduction of benchmarking into the NHS, outlining how the first year of activity concentrated on identifying the considerable variation in performance. The second year developed awareness of the benchmarking approach and establishing improved systems of comparative information. The third year has seen the adoption of a benchmarking approach to continuous improvement with a number of projects and partnerships well developed and quality and timely comparative data becoming available. The test for the future is to maintain the momentum and to see the realisation of results.

Whilst this review concentrates on health the lessons are important to other services. Many services in local governent aspire to excellence, for example Islington Council's logo is 'Aiming for the Best' and Essex County Council Social Services recently proclaimed in one of their adverts 'Delivering the best service means having the best training'. The vision is there but the achievement of the practice demands analysis of how to get there if vision statements are not to be simply platitudes. Benchmarking provides a systematic approach to achieving best in class status but even benchmarkers should ensure that they are 'really going places as distinct from continually redesigning the sails or reinventing the compass' (Griffiths R, 1991).

There have been two major revolutions in health in the last 10 years, the first came in two phases, the introduction of general management inspired by Sir Roy Griffiths' inquiry in 1983; the second phase was the introduction of the internal market by the Prime Minister, Margaret Thatcher after some well publicised illustrations of financial ineffectiveness in 1988.

The introduction of general management and the management of resources was not well received by the professions. 'There was a deep-seated feeling that what distinguished the health service from the private sector or business or commerce was the very immunity of the health service from the supposedly corrupting influence of profit-making and that this very immunity itself guaranteed high quality.' (Griffiths R, 1991).

This Sir Roy argued 'denies the fact that the hallmark of the truly great organisations in the private sector is that they have placed quality and customer satisfaction first and profit for a long time simply merged as a by-product of effective service. The truth is that it is the same attitude which gives top class quality and top class value – an obsessive wish to do things better.' (Griffiths R, 1991).

The introduction of the internal market coincided with the second 'revolution' in the sense of a cyclic recurrence. Back in 1919 the Health Act required the then minister of health to 'take all such steps as may be desirable to secure the preparation, effective carrying out and coordination of measures conductive to the health of the people'. The creation of the National Health Service in 1946 concentrated on access to adequate hospital care. 'In hindsight, general practice and public health were neglected grievously, cast out into the fields of worthy neglect as hospital medicine flourished.' (Widgery D, 1979 p 32).

Epidemiological and socioeconomic data had long suggested that Wales suffered a lower level of health than other parts of the UK or Europe. Heart disease and certain types of cancer were to be seen in higher proportions than in England. Health knowledge related behaviours such as smoking and pregnancies among young people were also demonstrably high. In addition the rural nature of much of Wales affected people's ability to access health services. Whilst there has been universal improvement the disparity in death rates remained almost the same from the 1930s to the 1970s (Rees and Rees, 1980 p 95). There was significant improvement in male life expectancy in the next decade and infant mortality rates fell by 40% between 1979 and 1989, but there were still notable black spots including the high incidence of death from circulatory diseases and cancers.

	Best ⟵		⟶ Worst		
	Top 25%	2nd 25%	3rd 25%	Bottom 25%	Number of Countries
Infant Mortality		● ○			24
Cancers		● ○			23
Thoracic Cancer		● ○			27
Breast Cancer				● ○	24
Ischaemic Heart Disease			● ○		24
Cerebrovascular (Stroke)		●○			24
Circulatory			●○		24
Maternal Deaths (per 100,000 live births)	● ○				24
Road Traffic Accidents	●○				23
Suicides	● ○				23

● Wales at 1989

○ Wales at 1981

Source: *Caring For the Future*, NHS Directorate, Welsh Office, December 1992.

FIG. 1.1 Causes of Death in Wales Compared to other European Countries 1981 and 1989

In the late 1980s the health service in Wales sought to redress this problem with the publication of an ambitious programme based upon the vision of improving the health, rather than the health services, of Wales.

'Working with others, the NHS should aim to take the people of Wales into the 21st Century with a level of health on course to compare with the best in Europe.' (Strategic Intent and Direction (SID), Welsh Health Planning Forum, 1989.)

The Wales strategic intent document established three key themes of strategic direction: health gain, people centred services and effective use of resources.

In 1990 the Secretary of State for Wales endorsed the *Strategic Intent and Direction for the NHS in Wales* as a definitive statement of the corporate goal of NHS and it has remained as a widely recognised mission statement for all staff working in the planning, delivery and monitoring of health-care in Wales. Its practical presentation is in the formulation of *Local Strategies for Health* based on local needs seeking to commission service responses covering prevention/promotion, diagnosis/assessment, treatment/care and rehabiliation/monitoring for key areas such as cardiovascular, cancers and maternal and early child health (Welsh Office, 1989a).

The approach was subsequently taken up in *Health of the Nation* for England. The Secretary of State for Health emphasising that 'setting objectives and targets for improvements in health is an essential discipline' but there is also the practical realisation that 'there must be a clear understanding of how the targets can be carried forward into effective action to meet them' and that 'targets should be set on the basis of what can be achieved through good practice' (DoH, 1991 p 15).

The document emphasised the need to concentrate effort on priorities and set out a format to highlight major causes for concern, scope for improvement and ability to set targets.

Area	Major cause of concern	Scope for improvement	Ability to set targets
Coronary Heart Disease	Greatest cause of Premature death	Healthy living	Yes, effective treatment

Source: *Health of the Nation*, p17.

The proposals for action focused primarily on improving health in terms of the incidence, prevalance and effects of disease. The document emphasises that the necessary refocusing of activity on the prevention of disease and the promotion of good health must not be at the expense of NHS treatment and care services. A better balance is needed, not a bias in one or other direction. To help ensure this balance is sustained in the health strategy the document proposes that in addition to the objectives and targets proposed for health, each health authority should set itself stringent 'quality of service' targets (DoH, 1991 p 10).

The NHS is therefore faced with contributing to health gain and to improving the quality of services. It is estimated that the health service only contributes about 30% of health gain activity. The rest is dependent on personal life choices such as eating, drinking, smoking and exercise, occupational health and risk, social and employment status and factors related to the availability of housing, education, transport and public protection (see WHPF, 1994).

The SID document recognises this by emphasising the need to 'work with others' to achieve the ambitious targets. The opportunities for benchmarking for health gain and the issue of balancing the purchasing and maintainance of existing service provision with the commissioning

	Understand Customers	Respond to Electorate	Consistent Achievable Objectives	Clear Responsibilities	Train and Motivate People	Communicate Effectively	Monitor Results	Adapt to change
Financial Systems		x		x				x
Management Processes	x	x	x	x	x	x	x	x
Communications	x	x	x	x	x	x		
Information Technology						x	x	x
Organisation and Structures			x	x				x
Staffing	x	x			x		x	
People Management	x	x		x	x	x	x	x
Top Management	x		x	x	x	x	x	x
Members	x	x	x	x		x	x	x

'Management arrangements relate to key success factors", Exhibit 3 in Annex D in *How effective is the Audit Commission?*, The Audit Commission for Local Authorities and the National Health Service in England and Wales, 1991.

FIG. 1.2

productivity and maintain quality means that these issues more than ever before need to be tackled together within a corporate strategy.

Corporate Strategy in the NHS

The NHS Corporate Strategy for Wales was first set out in the Five Year Corporate Management Programme in 1988 (Welsh Office, 1988). At the time it was published it placed the health service in Wales in a unique position by linking all the tiers of the service within a single planning and management framework. By 1990 there was a need to revise and explain the plan following legislative change and the publication of the Strategic Intent documents. *Agenda for Action: 1991–1993* was published in December 1990 to provide a new focus for the management of the NHS. The document noted the establishment of the VFM Unit and the introduction to health of the Audit Commission.

It was followed a year later by *Agenda for Action 2* (Welsh Office, 1992b). In this volume the pursuit of value for money was recognised as central to the *NHS Wales Strategic Intent and Direction*. The document argued that the responsibility for delivering VFM must remain with those most directly involved in the delivery of health-care services and must be a part of day-to-day activity. However a number of initiatives were launched to support VFM including the establishment of a clinical resource ultilisation group (CRUG) to address clinical resource issues, promote clinical efficiency, disseminate ideas and consider ways of encouraging new initiatives and also benchmarking which was then identified as the provision of management information to enable providers to compare their performance against those of top performers in England and Wales. A target to introduce benchmarking by February 1992 was established. In addition it was made clear that following the publication of the White Paper *Competing for Quality* (HM Treasury, 1992), provider units would be expected to pursue an active and expanding programme of market testing.

In December 1992 the pathfinder document *Caring for the Future* was issued as the NHS Wales strategy for a healthier Wales (Welsh Office, 1992c). Ten top prioriies were identified including promoting efficiency through 'the extensive use of benchmarking by commissioners, providers and professions to link performance to top performance in the UK'.

In March 1994 a new *Caring for the Future* was issued with a strong emphasis on quality, plain English and diverting money from administration to health-care. NHS Wales was set the challenge of succeeding in three fields, **ever improving health**: 'We are committed to making Wales one of the healthiest countries in Europe'; **outstanding service and real choice for patients**: 'A quality service is one which meets people's needs, satisfies or exceeds their expectations, and does so by drawing the best out of a range of skills and techniques'; and **steward-ship**: concentrating on what is of real benefit 'comparing our performance with the best is an essential aid to improving performance and quality' (Welsh Office, 1994 p 4).

The initiative sets out 10 commitments including the commitment to focus investment on effective services by finding out which services work best and only expanding the use of new services after rigorous evaluation. The documents encourages everyone in NHS Wales to deliver quality services by improving operational efficiency with 'more "compare with the best" initiatives throughout NHS Wales'.

Development of Benchmarking in NHS Wales

The benchmarking approach draws together the threads of quality and cost-effectiveness within a coherent framework but this is a framework which has had to be worked at. There have been four phases in the development of benchmarking, roughly corresponding to the annual financial cycle.

1. 1991/2: Opportunity cost model

2. 1992/3: Awareness

3. 1993/4: Adoption of approach

4. 1994/5: Implementation and results.

In parallel, the organisation has recognised the need to establish comparative data which can be used to support benchmarking efforts.

Phase 1.   1991/2: Opportunity Cost Model

The start to benchmarking was not auspicious: The Benchmarking Initiative was introduced to NHS Wales through the Annual Review process. This is one of the key tools used by the Welsh Office to realise accountability for health services in Wales.

An opportunity cost model was developed by the Health Intelligence Unit in the Welsh Office. Low cost hospitals of similar size and profile to Welsh hospitals were analysed to identify the potential for transferable cost savings. This methodology did not take root as although it identified on average £3m savings for each hospital it did not provide a means or incentive for the pursuit of improvement. It did however, have benefits in showing the way towards a broader and more structured approach. It highlighted the need for data and an understanding of 'look-a-like' organisations. The opportunity cost model approach is worth describing because there is now a revised enthusiasm. This is for three reasons:

The benchmark framework is now in place and the model can be used as a supportive tool since the motivation for examining variance is to identify good practice for improvement rather than seek statistical explanations to justify the status quo.

The quality of data has improved with the recognition that data submitted is useful.

There is a way of using the data as high performers can be contacted through the NHS Benchmarking Reference Centre.

Opportunity Cost Model: Benchmark Levels of Cost and Performance

The benchmark levels of cost and performance shown in the table were achieved in 1989/90 by hospitals among those classified as efficient in a comparative study. As not all specialities were relevant to all hospitals, the results were an amalgam of performance in a small number of hospitals.

Managers could compare their own figures with these 'benchmarks'. Some of the variation between units undoubtedly related to differing case-mix. However, these figures could be taken as a starting point for the investigation of variations in cost and performance. Of course the quality of service and the setting in which the service is delivered also needed to be considered. The treatment costs for patient treatment services were based on definitions for the FR12 specialty cost analysis returns. Hotel costs could be obtained from local sources or estimated from FR12 data after adjusting for the proportion of general services costs (less catering) attributable to patients not using a bed.

The system was based on two input tables which each unit had to complete, one for activity data for in-patients and out-patients (Table 1.1) and the second for cost and performance data (Table 1.2). These were then compared with a set of 'benchmark figures' (Table 1.3) to calculate the savings that could be obtained, other factors being equal, if the benchmark figures replaced the current figures with the same levels of activity (Table 1.4).

The results of the exercise are interesting. They suggest the example unit is cost effective in a number of specalities (where negative savings are shown), but there is room for improvement particularly in in-patients in geriatrics, other medical, orthopaedics and ENT and in out-patients for orthopaedics. The cost reduction benefit of matching the 'benchmark' hospital would be an annual saving of £3.7m. In some areas (geriatrics and most inpatients and most outpatients) however the tables suggest this hospital should be considered as a new benchmark.

TABLE 1.1   Input Activity Data for Unit No 1 1989/90

Speciality	Consultant Episodes	New O/P	Total O/P
Medical specialties:			
Paediatric	3550	1329	5502
Geriatrics	5447	443	5746
Other medical	9562	6936	38531
Surgical specialties:			
Gen surgery/urology	8578	4917	20108
Orthopaedics	3368	6023	16974
ENT	1354	3863	9375
Opthalmology	1545	4162	19175
Gynaecology	3311	3322	7149
Dental specialties	578	2045	6548
Maternity:			
Obstetrics	3378	2783	12010

TABLE 1.2   Example Input Cost & Performance Data

Specialty	Average length of stay (days)	Total: New O/P	Treatment costs I/P £	O/P £	Hotel £/day => costs
Medical specialties:					
Paediatrics	2.9	4.1	310.5	34.1	
Geriatrics	21.4	13.0	1174.6	25.0	
Other medical	5.9	6.0	513.8	35.0	
Surgical specialties:					
Gen surgery/urology	4.4	4.1	508.7	26.3	
Orthopaedics	5.7	2.8	631.0	27.9	
ENT	2.6	2.4	346.0	26.4	
Opthalmology	2.6	4.6	350.5	11.5	
Gynaecology	2.6	2.2	306.7	21.8	
Dental specialities	1.8	3.2	353.3	30.8	
Maternity:					
Obstetrics	4	4.3	430.0	18.6	

TABLE 1.3 Benchmark Cost and Performance Data

Speciality	Average length of stay (days)	Total: New O/P	Treatment Costs I/P £	O/P £
Medical specialties:				
Paediatric	3.6	4.8	397.0	37.0
Geriatrics	16.2	10.0	671.0	24.0
Other medical	6.5	7.7	374.0	43.0
Surgical specialties:				
Gen surgery/urology	6.0	3.2	548.2	33.0
Orthopaedics	5.5	3.4	426.5	23.7
ENT	2.1	2.9	234.0	38.0
Opthalmology	3.1	5.1	397.0	16.0
Gynaecology	3.2	3.3	359.0	34.2
Dental specialties	1.0	2.7	216.5	31.4
Maternity:				
Obstetrics	3.3	4.4	549.2	24.3

TABLE 1.4 Cost Savings from Benchmark Cost and Performance and Current Activity

Specialty	Reduced length of stay	Reduced treatment costs I/P	O/P	Fewer O/P Visits	TOTAL SAVINGS
Medical specialists:					
Paediatrics	0	−307076	−16199	−32456	−355731
Geriatrics	0	2743112	5523	31584	2780219
Other medical	0	1336385	−306381	−507022	522982
Surgical specialties:					
Gen surgery/urology	0	−338684	−134023	144329	−328378
Orthopaedics	0	688651	71324	−83050	676926
ENT	0	151619	−109117	−69453	−26951
Opthalmology	0	−71916	−86830	−32819	−191565
Gynaecology	0	−173094	−88973	−130425	−392492
Dental specialties	0	79042	−4069	32232	107205
Maternity:					
Obstetrics	0	−402546	−68374	−5715	−476635
All above specialties	0	3705493	−737119	−652795	2315580

The approach when applied to another 11 Welsh DGHs suggests savings would be possible in all but one unit with a range of 2% to 27%. The total value of savings is nearly £30m.

TABLE 1.5

Welsh Hospital	Total costs	Total savings	% savings
1.	29804291	2439484	8.19
2.	30607877	8366553	27.33
3.	18024340	2707764	15.02
4.	16156350	2105751	13.03
5.	18952741	2665472	14.06
6.	17371028	839467	4.83
7.	22282368	−109007	(0.49)
8.	16471271	3920450	23.80
9.	30805673	2177024	7.07
10.	16063260	380820	2.37
11.	18179376	4396126	24.18
	234718575	29889904	12.73

Phase 2.   1992/3: Awareness

In February 1992 a number of hospital general managers met in Llandrindod Wells to plan the approach for 1992/93. In March the VFM Unit issued a document titled *Benchmarking briefing* (VFM, 1992c) setting out the approach to be followed and the details of the steering groups which were to be set up for acute, community and teaching units, together with the criteria to be used for selecting look-a-like hospitals.

The approach was deliberately unit led to assist in gaining acceptance but in practice this delayed the process. However VFM were invited to discuss the concept at a meeting of Unit General Managers on 30th April. A guidance report (VFM, 1992b) was prepared and issued at that meeting but strong concerns were raised that the process of introduction must be managed by local units if it was to gain credibility and the activity should concentrate on process improvement rather than simply on performance. This was supported by the experience of successful benchmarking initiatives in the US and UK as presented at the 'Benchmarking for Competitive Advantage' conference held in Birmingham in April 1992 (Status Meetings, 1992) where it was argued that continual improvement in performance was achieved by a concentration on prioritised processes. The guidance notes were rewritten to indicate the concentration on processes relevant to the health service and the potential for local opportunities for action (NHSBRC, 1992b).

The VFM Unit established and agreed a six point plan to develop benchmarking.

1.   Awareness, training and support

2. Developing comparative data

3. Finding examples of best practice

4. Developing demonstration examples

5. Providing a mechanism for review

6. Identification of new areas to benchmark and the development of the approach itself.

1. Awareness, training and support

The VFM Unit developed the concept through guidance and good practice information, articles in the health-care press (including 'Best of the Best', *HSJ*, 27.8.92), training courses, management presentations, seminars, conferences, working groups and the development of benchmarking clubs. The November 1992 conference at Bridgend sponsored by consultants Arthur Andersen attracted 140 delegates and positive comment in the press (NHSBRC, 1992c). Benchmarking clubs were established to share and cooperate in developing best practice. The University Teaching Hospital has established a club to include a number of UK teaching hospitals with links to Ulm (Germany) and St Lukes (Chicago) whilst Morriston, Royal Gwent and Ysbyty Glan Clwyd established the first District General Hospital (DGH) club with Bradford, Southport & Formby and Swindon hospitals.

2. Comparative Data

Benchmarking requires high quality comparative databases to support the search for best practice performance. A number of initiatives have been established to support the identification of high performance and better practice. These included look-a-likes, patient episode data and high level indicators. These last two are explored in more detail in the chapter on comparative data.

Look-a-likes

The NHS Wales VFM Unit and the Welsh Office Health Intelligence Unit provided each acute unit details of look-a-like hospitals based upon a composite of statistics (primarily QS1 returns for 1990/91 corrected by reference to hospital and published yearbooks) (VFM, August 1992g). The District General Hospital look-a-likes were selected so that they were of a similar type (eg non-London, non-teaching and either acute or mainly acute) and of similar size (allocated beds within 10% of target hospitals). Each Welsh hospital was presented with a table of similar hospitals showing hospital name, district, total beds, a look-a-like score and details of daily available beds by

HOSPITAL	DISTRICT	BEDS	RANK	SCORE	SPECIALTIES
		371 YB: 383	0	0.00	13 SPECIALTIES GM: 97.80 PAED: 19.85 DERM: 7.58 GER: 37.88 GS: 98.18 ENT: 27.65 T&O: 39.43 UROL: 15.28 OR.S: 11.00 A&E: 11.23 ANAE: 1.60 HAEM: 5.13 PATH: 1.50
		385 YB: 410	1	69.32	13 SPECIALTIES 9 SIMILAR GM: 110.90 PAED: 11.60 DERM: 27.00 GS: 115.70 ENT: 23.60 T&O: 50.00 OR: 4.00 A&E: 8.70 HAEM: 6.60 NEUR: 0.30 OPH: 22.00 COR.C: 5.80 ITU: 6.00
		369 YB: 336	2	80.37	15 SPECIALTIES 8 SIMILAR GM: 73.80 PAED: 20.80 GS: 71.70 OPH: 16.10 ENT: 20.90 T&O: 67.20 UROL: 23.20 UNCL: 5.20 OR.S: 16.60 ANAE: 0.10 NEUR: 30.80 TH.M: 5.80 GYN: 0.10 TH.S: 14.90 AMEN: 0.60

FIG. 1.3   Benchmarking Look-a-likes

specialty. The look-a-like hospitals were listed in the order of decreasing similarity with the target hospital, using the nearest neighbour technique. Information on the specialty bed mix of the hospitals of similar type and size was used, after being adjusted by a scaling factor for each specialty, to calculate the 'distance' of each hospital in the subset from the target hospital, using Pythagoras. The scaling factors reflect the maximum number of beds in a specialty. The distance between the target hospital (T) and a particular hospital in a subset of similar size hospitals (A) is: $E_i(X_{iT} - X_{iA})^2$ where X_T is the number of scaled beds in specialty (i) in the target hospital (T) and where X_A is the number of scaled beds in specialty (i) in the target hospital (A) under consideration. The smaller the distance (or score), the more similar, in theory, the specialty bed mix. Additional information on outpatient attendances and A&E attendances was also provided to assist users to identify potential benchmarking partners.

The purpose of the tables was to assist hospitals looking for potential partners but they were advised to use other factors and personal knowledge too (see figure 1.3).

Welsh Health Information for the Comparison of Hospitals Project (WHICH)

Another development has been the Welsh Health Information for the Comparison of Hospitals project (WHICH VFM, 1992c). Data extracted from the central returns of all the major Welsh hospitals are analysed through a commercially available database, thus offering the facility of positioning Welsh units against agreed peer groups. A software package and printed reports are then analysed for information on relative performance, business planning needs and opportunities for data quality improvement. Pembrokeshire NHS trust and Ysbyty Glan Clwyd were the first hospitals in Wales to join the system as active members. A further five units joined in the first year with 10 more in 1993/4.

There was no comparable database for community units and there was a strong need to improve the consistency and completeness of cost comparison data. A similar project is intended to be developed with community health services and commissioning organisations.

A feature of this project has been the commitment to improving the quality and timeliness of data used for comparison and the shift away from comparison against averages towards best in class comparison. Data from other hospitals is anonymised but there is the facility within the service level agreement to obtain hospital consent to share further information and practices.

High Level Indicators

In May 1992 an NHS working group (HLI, 1992) issued guidance for in-year monitoring of management performance against a set of high level indicators. This minimum data set concentrated on provider performance and was designed to support the Annual Review of health authorities and their directly managed units. The indicators were recognised as an interim stage until a full set of indicators could be developed. This programme is discussed in the sections on comparative data and benchmarking clubs (Chapter 3).

3. Best Practice, Reference Centre and Overseas Links

A Benchmarking Reference Centre was established temporarily at Morriston Hospital in September 1992. Best practice examples were assembled and the centre began to coordinate data requests and visits to other units and organisations. Contacts were made with the Audit Commission, research institutions and consultancy firms. The Centre was soon able to collate and coordinate key interests from Wales and seek support from these organisations in finding and developing best practice.

VFM also began an active programme of seeking benchmarking partners in the UK and elsewhere. Links were made with hospitals in England, Scotland, Germany, France, the USA and Australia.

VFM also supported management trainee elective visits in 1993. Trainees have been invited to identify key process issues with their host in Wales and then to help identify best practice as part of their placement visits in the UK or overseas. This work is supported by Welsh Health Development International (WHDI) and MCS, the Organisational Development agency in the Welsh Health Common Services Authority (WHCSA). One of the first initiatives undertaken was a benchmarking of best practices in theatre utilisation with hospitals in Australia (Proctor J, 1993).

To encourage sharing of information and to avoid the excesses of 'medical tourism' the Centre adopted the international code of conduct for information sharing (see Chapter 3) and a guide to undertaking benchmarking visits (NHSBRC, 1992a).

4. Model Benchmarking Applications

VFM developed a number of model benchmarking applications, including initiatives on theatres utilisation, a patient flow initiative partly sponsored by Gwent Health (VFM, 1993a); development of community services organisational structures by Ogwr Unit; community services (dental services) costing by Gwynedd Community; pharmaceutical costs by University Hospital of Wales and a medical records review at Morriston.

5. Review

It was recognised that a 'mature' stage of benchmarking would see the approach integrated into business planning as a means to achieve success in key areas, as a focus for quality improvements and as a means to develop problem solving throughout the organisation. In the review carried out in Autumn 1992 (VFM, 1992d) it was clear that units were beginning to demonstrate this level of development, for example Glan Hafren recognised in their application for NHS Trust status:

'We have taken a lead role in initiatives in the Health Service in Wales in assessing efficiency levels through "benchmarking", a process designed to identify best practices and compare services.' (South Gwent Health Unit, June 1992 p 22).

6. Development of New Benchmarking Areas

The areas VFM suggested for development into 1993 include commissioning authorities, primary health services, ambulance services, scientific, hotel and support services and links between the benchmarking of processes and key cost drivers.

The review in September 1992 concluded that units wished for continued support from the VFM unit and the Reference Centre but with increasing involvement by health service managers. Managers asked for assistance in establishing benchmarking clubs; further training and advice and joint working on demonstration applications (VFM, 1992d).

1992 Conference

The first NHS Benchmarking Conference was held at Heronston, South Wales in November 1992 (NHSBRC, 1992c) see Fig 1.1. Attended by 140 health-care managers and practitioners it demonstrated that there was now an appreciation and commitment to benchmarking by senior staff in the NHS in Wales (Western Mail, Daily Post 19.11.92). Initial scepticism had been replaced by an understanding of the constructive and cooperative support offered by benchmarking in tackling a challenging management agenda. The concentration on a process-based and outward looking approach offered the potential for solutions from beyond traditional sources. The interest shown by units in England and Scotland had also encouraged senior managers in Wales to become

Introduction to conference
Jeremy Hallett, Chief Executive, Health Care Gwent

Benchmarking in Wales: an Overview
John Bullivant, Value for Money Unit

Benchmarking in Industry: Best Practice Lessons from outside health
Roger Davies, Manager of Operational Performance, British Airways

Achieving Best Practice Through Benchmarking
Michael Cowan, Arthur Andersen Management Consultants

REPORTS FROM THE NHS WALES WORKING GROUPS

Benchmarking 'Clubs': Teaching Hospitals Group
Roger Badman, Unit General Manager, University Hospital of Wales

Acute Units Working Group
Mike Naylor, Unit General Manager, Morriston Hospital

Community Units Working Group
Bob Hudson, Unit General Manager, Gwent Community and Mental Health Unit

OVERSEAS HEALTH

The View from the Outside Looking in
Pascal Garel, Attaché de Direction, Centre Hospitalier et Universitaire de Nantes

The View from the Inside Looking Out
Brian Davies, Chief Executive, Pembrokeshire NHS Trust

Purchaser Benchmarking
Sian Richards, Director of Performance and Corporate Affairs, Health Care Gwent

The Way Forward
John Bullivant, Value for Money Unit

FIG. 1.4 The First NHS Benchmarking Conference, Heronston Hotel, November 1992

personally involved to benefit from the peer group contact and sharing of mutual problems and their resolution. The priority for 1993 was the adoption of the approach and development of successful applications.

Phase 3.   1993/4: Adoption of Approach

The programme for the Benchmarking initiative for 1993/4 was presented to the Welsh Office in February 1993 (VFM, 1993b). Related work to develop high level indicators, to supervise the patient episode comparative data project and to encourage consistent costing of services were also agreed.

The objectives for 1993/4 were established as:

To consolidate the benchmarking initiative in acute and community services by supporting local initiatives through the reference centre and by selective sponsorship of individual projects;

To extend the initiative into new areas including
Commissioning Authorities
Ambulance Services
Scientific and Support Services including Pathology;

The development of the Reference Centre as a base for benchmarking initiatives in the NHS;

To seek to integrate benchmarking as a component of a new quality approach in the NHS in Wales.

Activity in 1993/4 was essentially one of consolidation in Wales and seeking out of benchmarking colleagues and partners and good practice in health and industry both in the UK and overseas.

NHS Wales has long realised that it cannot achieve its aims alone. The strategic intent approach emphasises the essential need of 'working with others' and benchmarking emphasises this in all elements of the approach whether process mapping, opening the door to the next department or to staff lifting their sights from the immediacy of their workplace to consider how others have approached and succeeded in tackling issues.

The NHS has pride in its work but the humility to learn from others and this has been reflected in the strong links now being established with industry and services overseas, particularly in Germany, France, Spain, Eastern Europe, North America and Australia.

The key achievements in 1993/4 were:

Adoption by Senior Management

Although there are still variations in understanding of approach, there is a recognition of the value of benchmarking. Although arguably a management jargon word it has become part of everyday speech. Several units now include benchmarking within management performance review. There is a new commitment to sharing of initiatives, information and skills within clubs. David Pokora, Chief Executive of Swindon Hospitals NHS Trusts put the case clearly:

'As a new Trust we will have an extensive workload ahead of us. We recognise that we cannot waste resources reinventing solutions already working for others. Benchmarking gives us the structure and the momentum to find and implement best practice to meet our commitment to be amongst the best. We have therefore joined our colleagues in Wales in working together to achieve improvements.' (1993).

High Profile

The approach has attracted considerable interest both within and outside the service. Wales is recognised as taking a lead in this area, strong links have been established with industry and health-care in the UK and overseas as well as with the All Industry Benchmarking Centre and the Wales Quality Centre. Joint projects with GKN Sankey, TSB and Welsh Water are being investigated. Common Interest Groups were established for customer satisfaction and supply chain management. A Benchmarking for Healthy Services Award has been established with sponsorship for 1994/5 by SmithKline Beecham.

Development of Comparative Databases

High Level indicators are now recognised as key service measures with UK-wide comparisons possible. They also provide a model for opt-in middle or department level indicators. The benchmarking clubs are taking a lead in collecting this information for mutual benefit.

The WHICH database provides DRG-based comparisons with UK peer group hospitals. Since December 1992, the VFM Unit has made over 100 visits to Welsh district general hospitals in connection with the WHICH comparative database project. By December 1993, 16 Welsh DGHs were actively involved in the project. Others are joining as soon as data transfer problems are overcome. Monthly visits were planned to continue through 1994/5.

International hospital comparisons were also being developed with direct links to hospitals in Spain, France and Australia.

Benchmarking Clubs
Clubs have been established in a number of groups. These are a means to an end but have been important in clarifying joint interests and objectives. The first groups were established in 1992 and further groups have now been established for district general hospitals, teaching hospitals, community units, ambulance services, pathology services, pharmacy services, commissioners and an international club involving hospitals in England, Wales, France, Spain, Germany, Australia and the USA.

Presentations
Over 100 presentations have been made to health-care organisations. In addition VFM staff have participated in a number of major benchmarking and quality conferences.

Publications
The *Benchmarking Briefing* has been established in conjunction with Longman, five editions are being produced a year. Good Practice Guides have been produced on a number of topics including, *Benchmarking Clubs* (NHSBRC, 1993a), *Use of Consultants* (NHSBRC, 1992d), and *Process Mapping* (NHSBRC, 1994).

Articles have been featured in the *Health Service Journal* and *Health Management*. The NHS Wales approach featured in Radio 4s *In Business* and a *Financial Times/Pitman* training video has been produced with examples filmed in operating theatres at Glan Clwyd (1994).

Benchmarking Development
A series of internal seminars have been organised to develop the approach and avoid duplication of effort within the service. These covered Benchmarking and Organisational Development, Benchmarking and Comparative Databases, Benchmarking and Clinical Audit, Remodelling Services: TQM, CIPs, BS5750, Benchmarking, Re-engineering and pragmatic management and Benchmarking and Health Gain.

Opportunities for Future Development

A number of areas including, commissioning, community units, some DMUs and ambulance services have been difficult to progress and will be given additional support through 1994/5.

The approach has tended to concentrate on the organisational unit of the hospital but increasingly requests for support have been coming from professional or discrete service groups. These groups which include pathology, radiology, pharmacy, medical physics and community dentistry will now develop as special or common interest groups.

Introduction

Dr John Bullivant, Director, Value for Money Unit

Welcome and Introduction

John Wyn Owen, Director, NHS Wales

Benchmarking in Practice

Mike Naylor, Unit General Manager
Ben Bennett, Information Manager
Dave Barham, Chief Dietician
Fiona Lund, Physiotherapy Department
Morrison Hospital, Swansea

Seeking Continuous Improvement in the Spanish Health Service

Aurelio Costa Suarez, Secretario General area de Salud de Alcoi, Valencian
Health Service, Spain

Benchmarking and the Patient's Charter

Judith Chadwick, Quality Manager, Basildon Hospital
Sam Cowgill, Assistant Quality Development Manager, Scarborough
Hospital

Seeking Best Practice in Pharmacy Services

Roger Badman, Unit General Manager
Mike Spencer, Director of Pharmacy
University Hospital of Wales

Benchmarking Clubs – What are they and how do they work?

Jonathan Parry, Chief Executive
Eric Chew, Director of Nursing and Quality
Southport and Formby Hospitals NHS Trust

Best Practice in Theatre Utilisation

Mr Roger Dunshea, Director of Information
John Proctor, Business Manager (Surgery)
Alison Hindmarch, Business Manager (Medicine)
Ysbyty Glan Clwyd NHS Trust

Learning Together

Ian Harrison, Director, Wales Quality Centre

FIG. 1.5 The Second NHS Benchmarking Conference, Cardiff International Arena,
November 1993

Related Work

The Unit is involved in a number of projects which have a direct bearing on developing benchmarking for the NHS. These include the High Level Indicators, Welsh Health Information for Comparison of Hospitals (WHICH) database, Patients Charter performance review, development of good practice maturity grids, resource releasing and overseas assignments which involve elements of benchmarking including an EC PHARE project training Bulgarian hospital managers.

1993 Conference

The second NHS Benchmarking Conference was held at the Cardiff International Arena in November 1993. Over 170 delegates from throughout the UK (plus visitors from Spain and Australia) heard how benchmarking has now been used in hospitals as a major support to improvement in clinical services and support services. Several delegates from local and central government attended and the organisers made a commitment to organise the next conference on the broader theme of 'Benchmarking for healthy services' to embrace all public services (Figure 1.5; NHSBRC, 1993b).

Development Work by Other Agencies in England

The Patient Charter Benchmarking Project was initiated by the NHS ME in 1992 with a full programme running through 1993. The approach originally involved 28 provider units collecting and sharing patient's charter performance data on a confidential basis. The techniques of benchmarking were explained to participants and opportunities for determining and sharing good practice developed. Interim progress was reported at the NHS Benchmarking Conference in Cardiff in November 1993 and a fuller presentation made at a Management Executive seminar held in Manchester in February 1994.

Developments in Australia

Benchmarking is already well developed in some hospitals in Australia, but there has been until 1994 no strategic focus and support. The Policy Branch of the Department of Health in New South Wales is however seeking to establish a framework for benchmarking which includes both the provision and sharing of key benchmark information as well as the development of benchmarking by service providers. To support this the Department has established partnership links with the State of Victoria and with the NHS Benchmarking Reference Centre in the UK.

Links with Australia are already proving fruitful, not least because of the common language and traditions in the health service.

Developments in the USA

Health-care in the USA has traditionally been seen as another sector of business and therefore fully integrated into the corporate management revolutions of the post-war years. Benchmarking is therefore well established both within hospital groups such as Sunhealth and between groups usually facilitated by commercial consultancy, eg the Ambulatory Surgery study sponsored by Arther Andersen (1992) or research organisations which are either health specific such as the Healthcare Forum, The Council of International Hospitals and The Joint Commission on Accreditation, or generic all industry services such as the International Benchmarking Clearing House and the Strategic Planning Institute (see Useful Contacts).

Phase 4. 1994/5: Implementation and Results

NHS Wales has adopted a mature version of benchmarking developed by industry and now established in most hospitals and services. The approach is based on senior management commitment to continual improvement of services to patients by integrating analysis of comparative performance with detailed understanding of the activity examined. Benchmarking as a systematic approach to finding and adopting good practice has proved an excellent means of drawing the many threads of change together.

The approach to benchmarking that has been adopted is consistent with the values and commitments expressed in *Caring for the Future* 2 (Welsh Office, 1994). In particular it supports the need for each part of the service to make a difference to health, to measure performance and change to achieve better value from existing resources, to focus on effective services and invest in systems that work and services of proven worth.

Summary and Directions for the Future

In summary the first year of activity concentrated on identifying that there was considerable variation in performance, the second year on developing awareness of the approach and establishing improved systems of comparative information, the third year has seen the adoption of a benchmarking approach to continuous improvement with a number of projects and partnerships well developed and quality and timely comparative data becoming available. One of the principal aims for the next phase of the initiative will be to develop the understanding and involvement of those health-care agencies still not yet using the approach. This applies particularly to commissioners, specialist services and our partners in other services and private health-care provision. In this way, there will be more scope to develop understanding of each other's processes and to identify key issues and priorities. The test for the future is to maintain the momentum and to see the realisation of results.

The priorities are therefore:

– achievement of results

– maintaining commitment and momentum

– more widespread awareness to support NHS Wales initiatives, 'we need others to help ourselves'.

Whilst this review has concentrated on health there is obvious application into other areas of public service. The NHS with its internal market has learnt to look from the inside outwards to adopt 'a businesslike approach'. The approach described here will therefore apply equally well within traditional areas of local and central government but also to organisations that as a result of next steps arrangements, competitive tendering or management buy outs now find themselves working from the outside in.

Chapter 2
The Benchmarking Approach

This chapter looks in detail at how to undertake a benchmarking project following the approach developed by Rank Xerox and adapted for use in the NHS. The approach follows 12 steps within three phases, Planning, Analysis and Action. The diagram reproduced from *Benchmarking Briefing* (Fig. 2.1) highlights that many of these steps involve familiar activities here brought together as a comprehensive programme for improvement.

Planning

First, select the subject area using SWOT analysis, internal or external reviews or audits or customer feedback. Check the issue has sufficient value and opportunity to warrant your attention. Check if the problem has a simple answer and just needs a decision (low hanging fruit) or needs an improvement team approach to plan and implement a known solution (high hanging fruit). If the problem appears intractable or too complicated for 'obvious' answers set out a simple process map of key output or outcome required and the 10 main elements which should lead to this output. Try and identify the failure points. Check if the solution is now obvious. Make a first assessment of potential best practice partners. Try and find 20–30. Identify the data required to make comparisons.

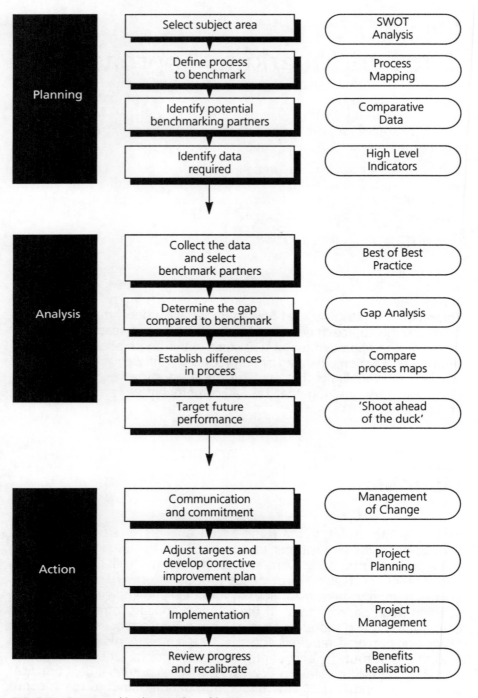

FIG. 2.1   Steps used in the Benchmarking Process

Step 1: Select Subject Area

Benchmarking should not be entered into lightly. It can be time consuming and will demand commitment from senior managers and operational staff. It helps if your organisation is committed to creating a quality driven organisation which seeks to meet purchasers, patients and clients needs. In this case benchmarking can provide a practical approach to deliver your vision but it can also be helpful in defining the key failure points frustrating success.

It is essential to concentrate on issues of importance to the organisation and to gain a return from your investment in benchmarking. Benchmarking should therefore be integrated into your business planning cycle rather than be run as a separate activity.

The first step in a benchmarking plan is to identify the key issues for your business or business area and to concentrate on these. You may already have had brought to your attention cost, quality or performance deficits or a significant shift in volume of work. Or, you may have actively sought to identify key issues for survival and success through SWOT (strengths, weaknesses, opportunities, threats) analysis or by constructing a maturity grid to assess current performance against best practice. An example of a maturity grid from a set of guides on waiting times developed by the VFM Unit in Wales is shown in Figure 2.2 below (NHS Wales, 1992b).

Care should be taken in the selection of projects, to ensure they are critical to survival, have sufficient value to the organisation and opportunity

KEY ELEMENTS	MINIMUM	GOOD PRACTICE	BEST PRACTICE
GP referral	Referral letter format agreed by consultants	Referral letter to state urgency, reason and provisional diagnosis	Referral protocols agreed between GP and consultants
Categorisation and prioritisation of patients	Categorise patients according to urgency	Categorise patients according to urgency and condition	As good practice and link to condition clinics
New outpatients appointments	Ensure appropriate mix of new and return patients	Organise specific clinics for most common conditions	Offer booked admission date
Inpatient treatment	Ensure efficient use of capacity to minimise turnover interval	As minimum with development of discharge procedures	Develop inpatient protocols, length of stay and discharge procedures by condition

FIG. 2.2   Maturity Grid for Managing Waiting Times

CRITICAL SURVIVAL/DEVELOPMENT ISSUES

BEFORE SUBJECTED TO MARKET TESTING

HIGH VALUE ISSUES

HIGH OPPORTUNITY ISSUES

FIRST TIME PROJECTS

FIG. 2.3   When to use Benchmarking

for improvement and are unresolvable by other means. The only exception to this is in undertaking the first project when you may wish to tackle something simple to gain experience and confidence.

Key to Business Survival or Development
The issue should be of strategic issue to the chief executive and board members or, within a department, to the senior management team. Performance may be considered acceptable internally because the approach works or meets internal targets, however external comparison or reference to client expectations may give cause for disquiet. Market testing will show relative performance; benchmarking provides a means to achieve levels equal to and surpassing the best.

High Value
The activity has either high cost, risk or prestige value, eg in a hospital the diagnostic services may be of relatively low cost but of key significance since if GP fundholders direct business elsewhere, the hospital risks losing patients who may also be referred elsewhere for treatment.

High Opportunity
The comparison of performance to best in class should indicate that local performance is such that there is considerable room for improvement in cost, productivity, quality or outcome. The desired outcome should be achievable and, if this is a first attempt at benchmarking, low risk since future activity will depend on success.

Unresolvable by Other Means
Benchmarking can help to clarify the issues, but is an extravagant way of confirming that unfinished business is still unfinished. Many issues can be resolved simply by giving them attention or following through on difficult decisions. Others may need the benefit of the attention of a multi-disciplinary team to aid both issue resolution and broad commit-

ment. Benchmarking is best reserved for those key issues where the problem is identified but the solution is genuinely not clear.

This can be presented with the hanging fruit diagram (Fig. 2.4).

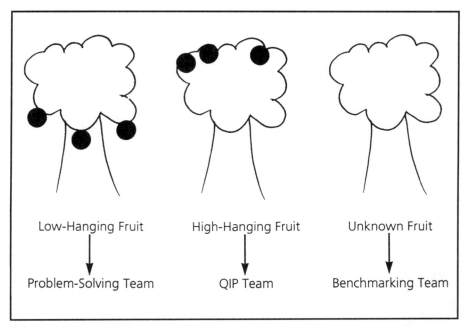

FIG. 2.4   Hanging Fruit

Low Hanging Fruit
This is when the problem (the tree) is clear and the solution (the fruit) is also readily available. Take the decision, pick the fruit.

High Hanging Fruit
This is when the problem is also clear but the solution whilst visible is less easy to take immediately. The best approach might well be to establish a quality improvement team who by involving all interested parties can best manage and communicate the change process.

No Tree, No Fruit
This is when you know there is a problem or issue that needs resolution but the nature of it is unclear and there are no ready answers. The temptation may be to bring in consultants or to invent a solution. This is when benchmarking is most useful because it starts by looking at the current activity and seeks to understand what is sought and what is being achieved now. The solution may be found by tackling failure

points, overcoming accidents at the boundaries of different functional groups or by looking at better practice elsewhere.

It may well be that using this approach quickly brings the problem and its solution into focus, in which case pick the fruit.

New Developments

Benchmarking is also a useful approach for new opportunities and to ensure that new initiatives, even whole hospitals, are designed from the outset to be world class. Where the activity is new and there is no process to map, you may find it helpful to roughly design the system as you think it will work, map it and then take a 'walk through' with colleagues who will be involved in providing the service. This will give them the opportunity to identify potential bottlenecks and failure points. At this stage you might consider visiting other locations who already provide the service successfully. The comparisons with your 'map' will highlight how to improve the activity whilst keeping the best of your teams ideas.

Conclusion

Benchmarking is not the right approach for every situation. In many cases the answer is simply to question existing practice or to make a decision. In some cases the problem and the solution are reasonably clear but ownership and communication are the key issues.

Benchmarking might not be necessary for the whole project. Benchmarking helps to highlight the real rather than the presenting problem. This is best achieved by mapping the processes which make up the activity under investigation. If the real problem is discovered and can be quickly resolved there is no need to continue.

Benchmarking is best used for the more strategic problems where solutions are not readily available. The more sophisticated process mapping noting time and cost of each element allows the approach to be developed into cost reduction and process re-engineering. The removal of process elements which fail to add value to the activity improves quality as well as reducing costs.

The detailed knowledge of our own organisation gained from process mapping allows us to gain the most from the best practice sites. It not only highlights where we need most help but makes clear where to make the changes when we find and understand higher performers.

The combination of top down strategic business planning with detailed bottom up analysis of process provides us with an extremely powerful approach to manage resources and business development. It also helps to develop local decision taking and empowerment by clarifying roles and responsibilities.

Step 2: Define the Process to Benchmark

The first step in benchmarking is selection of the subject area or activity to investigate. This will usually be an area of key significance to the organisation or department, with high value (cost, prestige or risk) and high opportunity, ie current performance falls far short of desired or best practice. This stage presumes at least some comparative information is available to make a judgement on the need for improvement. If comparative data is not available but there is cause for concern, proceed to the next stages and identify data collection requirements.

Having selected the activity area, the next step is to define the process to benchmark. In practice this usually requires a number of stages. (Fig. 2.5).

1. Define boundaries of activity
2. Clarify the desired outcome of the activity
3. Map the process elements undertaken now
4. Confirm functional responsibility for each element
5. Identify failure points. A key failure may be that the current practice fails to achieve the desired outcome.
6. Decide if failure points can simply be corrected, require search for best practice or more detailed mapping.

FIG. 2.5   Stages in Process Mapping

1. Define Boundaries of Activity and Clarify Customer and Currency

This can be most easily achieved by reviewing all the inputs and outputs of the activity. For example an out-patient clinic requires inputs of new and repeat patients and their relatives, enquiries, services, staff, accommodation, bookings and cancellations and records and produces outputs of patients, information and diagnostic requests, treatments, records, data, referrals to other departments, etc.

INPUTS	ACTIVITY	OUTPUTS
New patients		Patients
Repeat patients		Information requests
Relatives		Diagnostic requests
Enquiries		Treatments
Services	Outpatients clinic	
Staff		Data
Bookings/ Cancellations		Referrals
Accommodation		
Records		Records

FIG. 2.6

To make sense of all this establish the beginning and end of the activity, eg a study of outpatient booking arrangements might start when the referral is received, when a GP requests an outpatient appointment or when the patient arrives. The finishing point of the activity could be when the patient is first seen by a consultant, when the patient leaves the hospital or when the patient is discharged from treatment. It is important not to take on too large a topic at the outset; inevitably the subject becomes more complex with investigation, so a clear focus at the outset will assist in making the project manageable.

Try to clarify who is the 'customer' for the activity, eg it might be the patient or the GP or simply the next department, eg for an ambulance maintenance workshop it might be the emergency operations department who want the ambulance vehicle to be available for use next morning. Also clarify the 'currency' of the activity. It might be patients, pain, health gain, medical records, X-rays, vehicles or data. If this changes or splits during the activity ensure this is clear and, where necessary, there are separate tracks, for example, for patients and their records.

2. Clarify the Desired Outcome of the Activity

The desired outcome of the activity might be expressed as 'this activity is carried out *in order that* x will happen'. This may be further defined within a specified time span or within certain standards or resource limits. In the case of an outpatient booking system this might be: 'The outpatient booking system has been established in order to ensure that all patients are given an appointment within one month of GP request and are seen by a consultant within 30 minutes of their allotted appointment time'. More simply it might be that for all appointments the doctor, patient, test results and medical records are all present at the same time.

If there is no clear reason for undertaking the activity be prepared to question whether this work should be done at all.

What are Process Maps?

Process maps are pictures of the way that work (eg patients), information or paperwork flow through an organisation. The maps can be used to describe how work is currently done, or the way that a proposed new activity will work. Examples can be found in figures 2.7 and 2.8.

Why use Process Maps?

Process maps are an effective way of allowing the benchmarking team to quickly understand and document the chronological sequence of events and to understand the relationships that exist. Often these relationships are complex, are not well understood or are understood differently by different people. The maps help benchmarking teams to understand how things are really done rather than presuming that practice is logical or follows a written protocol. The maps help to identify where measurement is required and to focus on removing or improving failure points. They:

Develop understanding of process

Show chronological picture of the way work is done

Place responsibility for managing each process step

Indicate where to collect data or measures of performance

Identify failure points and redundant steps

Identify delays and waste

Focus process improvement resources

Promote trust

Promote ownership

Move process ownership to the *appropriate* level in the organisation.

3.   Map the Process Elements Undertaken Now

The next stage is to record a simple to understand map of the actions currently taken to achieve the desired outcome. It is important at this stage that the actual process is described *not* the protocol or preferred approach. Process mapping is best approached in a series of iterations, progressively more detailed. Always remember that the process map is not an end in itself, rather we are seeking to improve performance by finding and correcting failure points.

The first iteration should not have more than about 10 process elements or decision points. This is to ensure that the activity is clearly understood. If this is impossible the activity may be too complex and should be broken down into two linked projects. In the case of the outpatient booking system this might be the case with the need to define the process of booking the appointment as one activity and the process of ensuring the patient is seen within 30 minutes as a second activity.

4.   Confirm Functional Responsibility for Each Element

Look at the 10 elements and decide where the functional responsibility lies, ie which department. In an organisation fully structured to meet the needs of the patient these might well be all within the same department but this is rarely the case. At this stage it may be recognised that some key stakeholders have been omitted. Redraw the summary map trying to ensure that all stakeholders in the activity are included, eg GP, patient, relatives, ambulance service, medical records, consultant, outpatients manager, pharmacy, pathology etc. The role of some of these may be unfamiliar at this stage but it is often the lack of communication between functional areas which causes failure points at the boundaries between them.

5.   Identify Failure Points

A key failure may be that the current practice completely misses the desired outcome. If this is so, some drastic reorganisation may be required and benchmarking against others will be particularly helpful. If the outcome is achieved in part but performance is considered low compared to expected standards, concentrate on those process elements which contribute to this failure, ie do not at this stage be sidetracked by idiosyncratic behaviour which has little to do with whether you achieve the desired outcome or not.

An obvious failure point is the perceived lack of control over demand. If this is the case this must be tackled, either by seeking to prepare a flexible response which can handle fluctuations in demand or by attention to the cause of increasing demand. For example the cause of increased demand in A&E departments might well be long waits for elective work. The policy on elective admissions and the GP or patients response is therefore a contributory factor to be tackled. A common problem is that too many different agents can refer work and the role of the activity manager is unclear or ambiguous.

The problem may be that little information is collected within the process, for example whilst we may be measuring the failure to achieve the desired outcome it may not be clear which of the process elements are the culprits. To understand this may require some disaggregation of the data or temporary process element measures to be established.

For example the problem may be perceived as an excessively high length of stay, but no information is available as to whether this is pre- or post-operative. The first step would then be to analyse patient episode length of stay (LOS) data by distinguishing LOS from admission to operation date and LOS from operation to discharge. If the problem appears to be pre-operative, it might be necessary to investigate the turnaround time for diagnostic services. If post-operative, the delay might be caused by infrequent ward rounds, or the time taken to arrange medical records, prescriptions or patient transport.

6. Decide if Failure Points can Simply be Corrected or Require Search for Best Practice

If the first iteration identifies a clear failure point and the solution is obvious there may be no need to pursue the extended approach to benchmarking. If you can fix it, fix it. If the failure is one of not following the printed protocol remember it may be the protocol that needs changing as well as the practice that has grown up of circumventing it.

If the reason for the failure is less obvious, two responses should be considered now: either more detailed mapping, ie further iterations or a search for better practice elsewhere.

The decision as to which to pursue must be based on the particular circumstances. A general rule would be that there is little value in studying best practice elsewhere unless you are clear on how your own process works. Obviously there is a balance to be struck between more and more detailed mapping and the search for improvement. There is usually no need to map all of the activity to the same level of detail, the best approach is to use a pareto approach and to home in on the problem area and study that in more detail.

Detailed Process Mapping
The simple format for benchmarking was vertical with start at the top and the objective at the bottom. However any one starting to produce process maps in earnest will soon realise how complicated the maps become and how many pages they cover.

Messy process maps fail to achieve one of the key objectives of process mapping, clarification of the process. Some simple rules need therefore to be developed and these have been based on practical experience

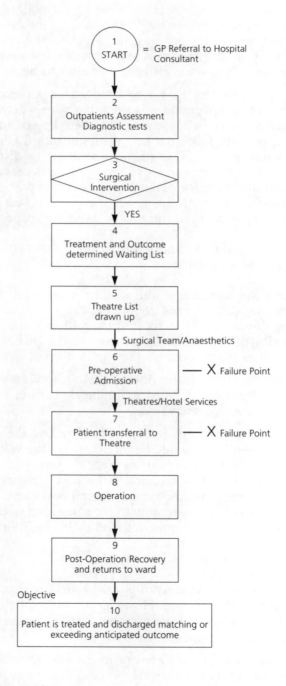

FIG. 2.7 Process mapping

within NHS Wales (NHSBRC, 1994b) at Cranfield and by the patient care teams at St Vincents in Melbourne.

The first rule must still be to keep it simple with clear boundaries of the activity under investigation. To improve presentation it is best now to switch to a horizontal format. This allows more information to be presented on the page and more text to be included in the process elements. A standard format is five elements across the page with a connector at each side to join pages or rows (Figure 2.8).

Each element should be annotated by the team or staff category responsible.

This format allows complex process maps to be produced and documented in tidy A4 folders. A number of software packages are available (eg *Chartist* or *ABC Flowcharter*) or the charts can be simply produced using the plastic Helix templates.

The great advantage of this format is that the charts can now be used to highlight time and costs and non value added elements can be readily highlighted for removal. The plan for the re-engineered process can also be readily compared. Point of data collection can be highlighted and volumes attached to the graphs.

Remember that at this stage the purpose of producing the maps is to improve the process, not just to produce the maps. Mapping should not become an industry or an attempt to wallpaper the office and greater level of detail should be reserved for greater understanding of failure points.

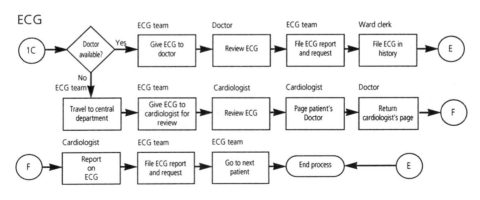

Source: St. Vincents, Melbourne

FIG. 2.8

Step 3: Identify Potential Benchmarking Partners

The benchmarking partner is the 'best' performer we can find at the process we are interested in, not necessarily best overall.

Benchmarking partner is a term reserved for the best in class organisation that you wish to emulate. It is important to distinguish between the benchmarking partner and the club or common interest member. Perhaps confusingly the literature has developed with the view that the partner is the external best practice comparator, ie the organisation that you are seeking to learn from. We therefore need a team for the fellow traveller in the search for best practice. Benchmarking 'colleagues' are the organisations that you work with jointly in the search for best practice, the self help group who belong to the same club or common interest group and who may or may not have best practice to share with you but are interesting in cooperating (see Benchmarking Clubs in Chapter 3.)

There is enormous value in working with benchmarking colleagues but only if the commitment is to action rather than unfocused discussion. Six departments or six organisations who commit to sharing data, knowledge and skills are more powerful than one. They have broader networks and often variation in performance and methods of working which is the ideal basis for comparison.

However whilst 'a problem shared may be a problem halved' in terms of your personal burden it is not a good idea to emulate your colleagues only slightly better performance and there is a danger in feeling comfortable with the collective mediocrity.

The value of benchmarking against the best is in raising sights to levels of performance thought unthinkable.

Can We Find the Best?

The answer is probably that we won't today but we will find someone significantly better, ie the 'best' available and with a commitment to continuous improvement we will no doubt eventually find someone better still and the next time we will find it easier to match and surpass them too.

Benchmarking partners can be found within our own organisation (internal partners); in other organisations in the same sector, eg another school or hospital (external partners) or finally we might look at any organisation that demonstrates superior performance regardless of the business sector (best in class partners).

The approach is broadly the same, the choice of type of partner dependent on the issue and nature of your organisation. Hospitals for example often have many departments undertaking the same kind of work and it would be relatively easy to arrange to compare performance and practice between different outpatient departments or clinical 'firms'.

Many organisations such as ambulance trusts have recently merged and therefore have the opportunity to compare practice between the old geographically based services.

External and best in class benchmarking may be more difficult to organise but has the potential for greater improvement. Most organisations specialise in particular services and the best can be expected to excel in their chosen field. Many public sector services have developed support services either by accident or through a reticence to use staff they do not control. Improvements in say transport services might be achieved by competitive tendering or more simply by comparison or market testing with the best. In either case the internal or external supplier will in future find it difficult to escape comparison.

Choosing Benchmarking Partners

First you must understand your own process or you may be seeking a partner who is good at the wrong thing (see step 2 above). If your area of interest is too broad and ill-defined, the search will be expensive and frustrating to you and those supporting you.

Seek a large group of partners who are better at the particular process (20–30). These may be identified at this stage by any means available but you should set a deadline of 2–4 weeks on this first stage. Use a brain-storming approach and all available contacts, benchmarking clubs and associates, agents, clearing houses, conference speakers, literature searches, annual reports, newspapers, comparative databases and publications such as the directories of quality initiatives and good practice produced by local government and health service agencies (see Sources). Use the 'Connections' column in the newsletter *Benchmarking Briefing*. Talk to suppliers and not just suppliers of goods.

For example a hospital which identifies from its risk analysis the communications and operational problems likely if the water supply is cut off, might wish to compare contingency plans with a nuclear power station or an airport. However the most appropriate help should come from the water supply company who may well have had to deal with the problem before and with the benefit of hindsight can either recommend better practice or identify another hospital who, having suffered before, has now got it right.

District health authorities are required to inspect private nursing homes. If they are interested in improving their practices, they could ask one of the national nursing homes organisations whom they consider to be most effective in their inspections.

Do not go and visit any of the potential partners yet. The final choice of benchmarking partners will require seveal iterations of the benchmarking plan to refine the short list of partners, but you should at this stage try and identify the criteria and the data that will confirm not only best performance but usefulness and reliability as a benchmarking partner. Consult the Code of Conduct and be prepared to abide by its guidance. If the potential partner is a competitor or has links with competitors ensure that all parties are likely to abide by the code.

Figure 2.9 shows a partner selection table at the early stage of looking for partners. The AB school has a problem with high levels of truancy. This has been identified in an inspector's report and the headmaster believes this is related to weak supervision and record keeping in the school. The XY school in the same County has a very high reputation generally and its thought to be better than most at containing truancy as they were interviewed and applauded on a *World in Action* programme. The headmaster of the XY school is known to the headmaster of AB school and they have cooperated previously on a 'stop vandalism' project.

Process: unplanned pupil absence Potential benchmarking partner: XY school			
Selection criteria	Weight	Score (1–10)	Weighted Score

Basis of comparison (10)
   reputation
   known performance
   process comparison
	
	5
	10
	20
		
		10
			
			50

Assessment (10)
   better than us
   better than most
   best in sector
   best in class
	
	5
	10
	20
	30
		
		8
			
			80

Relationship (10)
   Existing contact
   Prepared to cooperate
   Reliable partner
	
	5
	10
	20
		
		10
			
			50

TOTAL			180

FIG. 2.9

The score is not high with 180 out of a possible 700 yet at this stage it is a promising first start. The headmaster will not visit the school yet but has spoken to the headmaster who says he is also concerned with growing levels of truancy and has a number of contacts he made from the panel discussion on the TV programme, including meeting a freelance inspector from another County who had knowledge of truancy control systems in Scotland. The relationship score has now gone up to 100, and it seems they may be able to find best in sector practice.

Step 4: Identify Data Required, Sources and Appropriate Method of Collection

Benchmarking requires you to know your own organisation but it also requires comparison to know whether your activity is good or poor relative to the best. There is of course plenty of data available but not much information. It is important therefore at the first iteration of the benchmarking process to take stock and apply some 80:20 pareto principles. Use the data available, think laterally and set a definite date when data collection will be completed. Only start new data collection exercises as a last resort.

Check that you have completed the first three steps in your benchmarking planning. You should have identified a key problem and defined the objective and boundaries of the problem. Your value and opportunity analysis will have confirmed that it is worth proceeding. You have reviewed your own practice and identified failure points and points of current data collection. You will also have identified some potential benchmarking partners whom you think perform better.

If you have not got this far go back and review the process map even if it is only the first stage 10 activities and decision points which are supposed to lead to the desired outcome. Mark the failure points and identify if there is currently any data collection undertaken. Check for both formal statistical returns and local informal or 'shadow' data collection. Sadly formal data collection is often for purposes other than operational management of the process. However the person doing the job (the process owner) may well have established a routine of data collection or inspection which measures performance. Be prepared for untidy 'back of envelope' analysis; the process owner is unlikely to have had a budget for expensive computer systems for this work, they are just trying to do their job. If no information is available ask questions. Does it work? How often does it go wrong or do people fail to turn up? Do you reject 1 in 10 or 1 in 100 supplies?

Check that the data collection is on the right side of the activity. Too often we have good information on what we ordered whether its supplies or operations but less on how many were delivered successfully.

Use the Available Data

Remember you already collect a lot of data, but you may not be using it. Centrally held databases do not invent their data. It is supplied by operational parts of the organisation. Often this task is delegated (or relegated) to a junior member of staff and the whole process is discredited because the process is slow and unreliable. You know your data is suspect, so why should anyone elses be of any value. Large centralised data monitoring exercises may take several years to complete and if published or distributed the data is often of little value because it is neither timely nor accurate. You may wish to improve this process by introducing benchmarking to your colleagues and the data collection organisation itself. Point out that if you are actually using the data this fact alone will improve its timeliness and accuracy. However in the meantime see if the data you are collecting is useful and check with your benchmarking associates or partners if they will cooperate by sharing this data more quickly than waiting for a central return to be published.

You can short circuit the system by introducing two simple steps (Fig. 2.10).

If you need to undertake a new data collection exercise use the members (associates) of your benchmarking club if you have one, agree common definitions, rationale and formulas and only collect the data for the time you need it. Consider the cost of data collection. It can be expensive to start a data collection exercise but it is very expensive if you never stop. You may want to have a data item rule which says if I am to collect one more data item, then something else must go.

If you do not have an appropriate data collection system for the process you are investigating you may have to make assumptions from the high level to the specific. For example you may have access to a comparative database for hospital or schools but not organised by department. You are concerned about nurse absence in the orthopaedics department but only have comparative data by whole hospitals. The first step may be to compare on a whole hospital level but first check whether in your hospital your department mirrors the hospital average.

If you have a benchmarking club you can try and agree with your associates to collect some specific data for six months. You may consider broadening the exercise to others. The way to do this is not to simply send out a broadcast questionnaire or data collection request, but to first pilot the requirements by establishing the exercise with your six

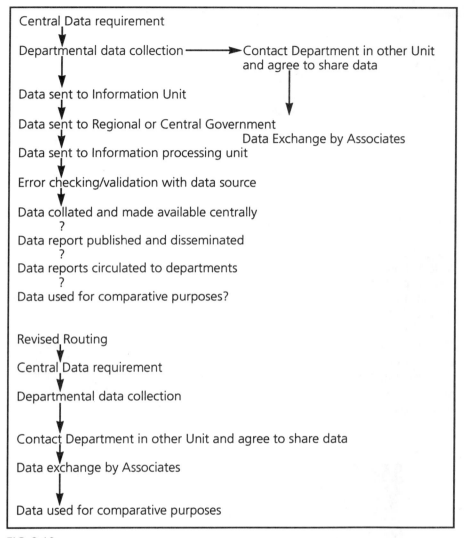

FIG. 2.10

associates and then offer to share the data to those who cooperate by sending in their data. You may use the facilities of a broker or reference centre for this exercise to maintain confidentiality within the code of conduct.

Successful benchmarking depends on being able to secure data on best practices which are suitable for comparison. In time the working through of benchmarking projects will help establish the requirements of systems and the benchmarking database will be established for continuing improvement. The ultimate data collection exercise is to visit benchmark partners. Remember therefore that you need to collect information which will identify and inform your choice of partners and their willingness to cooperate. Visits must be carefully planned in order that benefits are maximised for both organisations and information should be freely exchanged. For example, where one partner provides data it may gain by receiving data on another 'best practice'. The taking of a prepared process model to the best practice site may be a fair exchange for information on the development of one of their processes.

Analysis

Collect the data required, if possible have other departments or organisations collect the same data. If potential benchmarking partners already have a performance measuring system in place consider adopting their definitions for ease of comparison. Compare the performance and review best in class performers (5–10). Select preferred partners (2–3) and seek agreement to cooperate. Determine the gap between your performance and that of the selected partner (1–2). Assess the value and opportunity of proceeding. Is the solution obvious? Send or take the process maps to the partner(s) and identify the difference in process. Review the value and opportunity potential to apply in your situation. Target the performance level you will aim for.

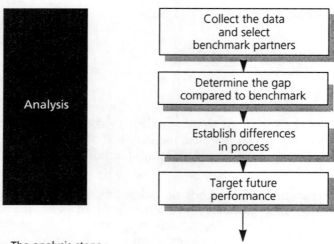

FIG. 2.11 The analysis steps

Step 5: Collect the Data and Select Benchmarking Partners

Once the data that needs to be collected has been identified, agreement within the benchmarking team should be reached on the data sources, internal and external, which are most likely to produce the information specified. Responsibilities must be assigned for collecting data and agreeing methods to be used, eg accessing databases, analysing medical records, telephone calls, interviews, visits, etc. It is important to establish a timetable for review and completion dates within the data collection exercise. When all the data has been collected the findings should be communicated to other members of the team and agreement reached regarding the next steps.

From the data collected, it should be possible to decide whether potential partners are indeed suitable, or whether they may have to be discounted, and a search for new benchmark partners undertaken.

Figure 2.12 below shows a partner selection table at the mature stage of looking for partners. The AB school has a problem with high levels of truancy; a high performing potential partner has been found. Agreement has been reached on cooperation and a visit has been planned.

Process: unplanned pupil absence Potential benchmarking partner: XY school			
Selection criteria	Weight	Score (1–10)	Weighted Score
Basis of comparison (10) reputation known performance process comparison	5 10 20	8	80
Assessment (10) better than us better than most best in sector best in class	5 10 20 30	8	160
Relationship (10) Existing contact Prepared to cooperate Reliable partner	5 10 20	8	80
TOTAL			320

FIG. 2.12

The score is now 320 out of a possible 700. Five other potential partners have low truancy figures and on the selection criteria scores of between 250 to 300. Three have agreed to cooperate and have been sent details by AB school of the study, definitions used, process maps and performance at AB and a list of the questions to be asked. At this stage one school wrote back and said they used a different definition and suspected they were not as good as published figures suggested. They would however like to be informed of progress.

Benchmarking Visits

Sound knowledge of the process in question will allow the visiting benchmarking team to ask the right questions to find not only 'what' best practice is being achieved but 'how' it is being done. The involvement of top management is essential to ensure that the process is correctly perceived as being of potential benefit to both partners. It may be easier to obtain competitive benchmarking information from further afield as rivalry between organisations in different locations or countries is often not so intense as between those in the same immediate market.

The involvement from the outset of top management and process owners who know the function intimately should mean that all the right questions are asked and answered, and that data is put to most effective use.

A key factor in information gathering and analysis is to 'shoot ahead of the duck'. Change is continuous, so as well as establishing where best practice is today the benchmark team must project forward the performance levels they will need to be attaining by the time the study is completed. It can be advantageous to maintain a benchmarking team to track the evolution of best practice and to ensure that performance measures are continually updated.

Step 6: Determine the Gap Compared to the Benchmark

Analysis of all the data from the benchmarking surveys, visits and other research will provide a wealth of material from which to identify the gap between your current process performance and best practice performance. However it is at this stage that you need to be scrupulously honest with yourself. It is all too easy to fall into the trap of excusing the variation for all sorts of imaginative reasons.

The ability to recognise poor performance and not be despondent is one of humility not humiliation. Concentrate on the positive of finding better performance and the opportunity that brings, rather than dwelling on the mistakes of the past.

Do not take the statistical variation on face value. The next stage will consider the variation in process, but here you should be concerned that you are comparing like with like.

The example given here (Fig. 2.13) is drawn from the WHICH project using information contained in the CHKS comparative database. With an average of 26 days length of stay for cerebrovascular disorders, this hospital is losing many bed-days against its UK peer group. American lengths of stay for the same disorder are almost half the UK ones for the same DRG. Further work could reveal the reasons for this and suggest cost effective and resource releasing changes for this patient group.

Bed Days Lost vs. Peer Group		No. of	Hosp	Peer	Days
DRG	DRG Description	Inpatients	Ave LOS	LOS	Variance
14	Specific cerebrovascular disorders except TIA	164	25.93	13.40	−2055.53
184	Esophagitis, gastroent & misc digest disorders age 0–17	211	5.11	2.42	−566.60
59	Tonsillectomy &/or adenoidectomy only, age >17	57	8.42	2.56	−334.24
12	Degenerative nervous system disorders	23	24.78	14.20	−243.39

Bed Days Lost vs. Ave US LOS		No. of	Hosp	Peer	Days
DRG	DRG Description	Inpatients	Ave LOS	LOS	Variance
14	Specific cerebrovascular disorders except TIA	164	25.93	7.50	−3023.00
127	Heart failure & shock	179	12.40	6.20	−1109.19
209	Major joint and limb reattachment procedures	124	17.64	12.30	−661.80
184	Esophagitis, gastroent & misc digest disorders age 0–17	211	5.11	2.40	−571.60

FIG. 2.13   WHICH project data

Step 7: Establish the Differences in Process

Once the performance gap has been identified and with a clear understanding of the process which is being benchmarked, it is possible to establish the reasons for differences in performance. Take your process maps to your benchmarking partner and work through the differences in process, the reasons for these differences, and ideas on how the performance gap can be closed. Make notes to identify and describe the differences and try and draw an improved process map, making notes of the changes involved. Remember you are trying to learn from their processes not copy them. The system must work in your location and you must take into account local circumstances.

OVERALL SUMMARY

Steps	Total	Process	Logistics	Queue	Record	Communication	Failure Points
Current							
Proposed							

	Current	Proposed
Documents		
IT Interfaces		
Job Descriptions		
Departments		

Departments/Staff Involved

Current Dept	Current Job Des	Proposed Dept	Proposed Job Des

OPTIONS/OPPORTUNITIES

Staff

Process Steps

Quality/Productivity/Cost Improvement

FIG. 2.14

You may find the partners say 'we used to do that but changed'. Find out why and try and understand the process of change as well as the end point. Learn from them what went wrong, because you can learn from their mistakes as well as their successes. Learning from others is surprisingly difficult and it is easy to be overcome by the complexity or to be awed by the mountain of effort that appears in front of you to achieve best practice. Take the process systematically and in measured steps.

You may find it helpful to draw up comparative tables of the two versions of the process, theirs and yours. Figure 2.14 is adapted from one used in work undertaken in St Vincents Hospitals, Melbourne and helps to establish the number and types of process elements being undertaken and by whom. Analysis of the completed table will help to determine the scale of change and where priorities exist.

Step 8: Target Future Performance

Analysis of the benchmarking data should show the relative positions of the benchmark partners now, and can be extrapolated to predict the future performance gap.

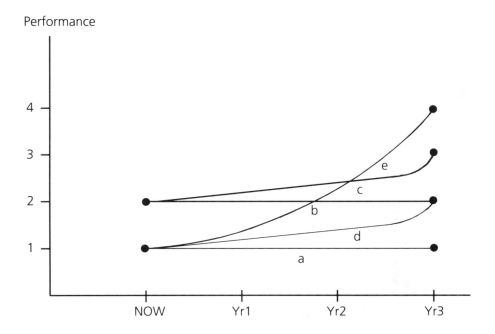

Performance

Key:
a= your performance — static
b= your competitor — static
c= your competitor with improvement
d= your performance with improvement
e= your performance with improvement and benchmarking

FIG. 2.15

Practices are not static. Both your own organisation and competitiors continue to pursue improvements. Therefore, you must not only analyse the benchmark gap as it exists at the time of measurement, but also project where the benchmark and gap are likely to be in the future. Shoot ahead of the duck and you might hit it. From an understanding of the process and the performance gap, action plans and budgets can be set to move towards best practice. You should surpass others' performance because you have learnt from their mistakes as well as their successes. How effectively best practice can be implemented however depends on the management of change, commitment and good communication (see Figure 2.15).

Action

Ensure all involved understand what is happening and confirm commitment of senior managers, purchasers, gatekeepers, process owners and consumers. Plan and manage the change with clear outline of roles and responsibilities, targets, milestones, timescales, benefits and costs. Implement the change with constant review of progress and value and opportunity of proceeding. When completed review outcomes in relation to expectations and consider opportunity for further improvement. Congratulate everyone involved and tell everyone who wasn't.

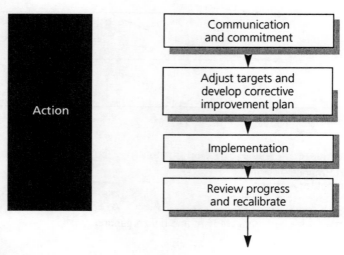

FIG. 2.16

Step 9: Communication and Commitment

Maintaining commitment over a lengthy period of time is not easy. If early results have not been achieved it may be difficult to hold the resources together to complete the project. New demands and opportunities will emerge which will divert key staff from the project. Added to this, analysis of the failure points which prompted the need for a benchmarking project in the first place often relate to 'poor communication'. It will not be surprising therefore that it is at this critical point of preparing for implementation that benchmarking projects can fail.

Critical to successful benchmarking is the gaining of acceptance from senior management and staff, firstly to embrace the overall concept and secondly to act upon the knowledge that there are higher standards to be reached and better ways of doing things. This is the building up of the commitment to continual improvement described as the first benchmarking intent.

The approach needs to be explained carefully and comprehensively and progress communicated to all staff.

Effective communication will:

- Secure commitment

- Gain cooperation.

A significant advantage of adopting change through benchmarking is that the process is already proven elsewhere and the method of achieving the desired results can be clearly demonstrated.

The opportunity to explore similar processes in different types of organisations can be helpful in reducing the threat of change for staff. Staff may feel more at ease in their own role by adopting ideas from a completely different organisation for example from an airline to a hospital whilst they may feel more threatened by successful new methods from another hospital. The need to learn from similar organisations suggests a criticism of their efforts and opens the prospect of new people coming in to implement change. Central to successful benchmarking therefore is the encouragement of existing staff to be involved in problem solving and implementation.

If communicated effectively benchmarking can provide a powerful motivator for change since:

- The gap between present and Best Practice promotes dissatisfaction and desire for change;

- Seeing, understanding and learning from Best Practice helps to identify what and how to change;

- Utilising Best Practice provides a realistic achievable picture of the desired future.

Obtaining the commitment of staff and colleagues is vital to the success of a benchmarking project. This is not always easy, but can be achieved through effective communications, clear explanation and regular updating of progress of the benchmarking process and its benefits.

It is worth remembering to include the patient in this communication programme. The most important message from a recent study in health (Audit Commission, 1993) is that senior professionals and hospital managers must develop an understanding of what it is like being a patient in their hospital. The same problem of 'how do you get your staff to retain the mindset of the customer after they have gone behind the counter' has been recognised and tackled by banks and other services (Cliffe R, 1993). Several hospitals and clinics have now responded to criticisms not only by dealing with them but by putting up a sign saying the changes are a response to visitors comments. This has the effect of informing patients of improvements which may not always be obvious but also conveys the message that you value their comments and will act on them.

Step 10: Adjust Targets and Develop Corrective Improvement Plan

It is important at this stage of the benchmarking process to stand back and review the organisations targets and goals. These may have changed since the project was first undertaken and since benchmarking should support the overall direction and objectives of the organisation, it is important to check that these goals are still relevant to the overall direction of the organisation. Failure to recognise changed goals and new priorities will obviously weaken the benchmarking process and the organisation itself. It may be at this stage that you set a much more ambitious target than orginally envisaged. The effort of implementation may be no more for a quantum leap than a small step. However develop the plan of corrective action with care. Use project management techniques like PRINCE (1990) to help organise major changes, clarify roles and responsibilities and to establish the milestones as well as the final deliverables of the project.

With most public sector services the plan must take into account the maintenance of the existing services as well as the planning of the new. This will take some careful organisation and deployment of resources.

Prepare for unexpected problems, learn if possible from the implementation errors and near misses of others.

Step 11: Implementation and Monitoring

The continued use of benchmarking requires a clear indication of successful implementation and measurable benefits. Both will be more readily achieved if the programme has clearly defined objectives within given timescales. The new processes and approaches being introduced are more likely to be implemented if there it top management commitment to the change, a key sponsor to support the development and a dedicated team working to achieve successful implementation. Sustained communication of progress to all staff will assist in developing understanding and support.

It is important that a senior manager holds responsibility for the business process under review and the development of best practice for that process. This may require a special assignment outside of traditional line management structures. For example to improve the process of 'getting patients home after discharge by consultant'. The manager has responsibility to see through implementation and has a high profile commitment to maintain progress towards success. A benefit of this approach is that the manager will have early warning of new factors which will affect the project or the need to adjust targets in line with new commitments or competition.

New monitoring requirements may be necessary to confirm that change is proceeding in the right direction. This data requirement may be temporary but the approach described in the comparative data section (Chapter 3) of clear definition, rationale and formula will ensure that useful data is collected and that staff know why it is being collected.

Step 12: Review Progress and Recalibrate

In order to measure the benefits of a benchmarking project it is necessary to review the progress of the project, not only at its conclusion, but throughout the benchmarking process. Without regular review, it will be impossible to tell what has been achieved.

Recalibration of benchmarking programmes is vital in keeping abreast of developments in the evolution of practice. Frequent attention should be paid to any performance measures being used to ensure they are still appropriate. These should be fed back into the benchmarking process to keep it up to date. The steps of benchmarking should each be systematically reviewed to identify deficiencies in the process and implementation of benchmarking. Recalibration not only refines the output of the process but can make the process more efficient and responsive.

Benchmarking is a process of continual improvement, more of a journey than a destination. At the outset of a project it will be difficult to see this and the focus will, quite rightly, be on achieving the desired target.

Once the programme has been completed and the benefits set have been realised it is of course the time for congratulation but it is also the best time for reflection on whether the best of the best has truly been achieved or whether greater heights are now within reach. The confidence of success will bring the confidence of greater achievements and this is the hallmark of a truly successful organisation. Check the value and opportunity equation again and if there is value in proceeding, go for it, it may be more like low hanging fruit now.

Chapter 3
Benchmarking Good Practice

There are many models of benchmarking and most of them are useful approaches to follow. It is important however that we adopt the principles of benchmarking for benchmarking itself. There is no need to reinvent benchmarking in every organisation, better to learn from others and adapt the approach to suit our own needs. The following sections on codes of conduct, benchmarking clubs and benchmarking visits are based on the experience of those seeking to use benchmarking in their organisations. The section on comparative data describes in detail some development work in the NHS in Wales as an example of an attempt to break out of the sad cycle of rubbish in, rubbish out so common in information gathering exercises. Finally maturity matrices are described as a simple means of identifying and auditing minimum standards, good and best practice.

Codes of Conduct and Benchmarking Protocols

Introduction

To guide benchmarking encounters and to advance the professionalism and effectiveness of benchmarking, the NHS Benchmarking Reference Centre, the Benchmarking Centre Ltd, The International Benchmarking

Clearing House and the Strategic Planning Institute have all adopted a common Code of Conduct (NHSBRC, 1992a).

I would encourage all organisations and individuals involved in benchmarking to abide by this Code of Conduct. Adherence to these principles will contribute to efficient, effective and ethical benchmarking.

To assist in the application of benchmarking, protocols for use of the code and for undertaking benchmarking visits are included at the end of this section.

Benchmarking Code of Conduct

Individuals agree for themselves and their organisation to abide by the following principles for benchmarking with other organisations.

1.   Principle of Legality

1.1   If there is any potential question on the legality of an activity don't do it.

1.2   Do not extend one benchmarking study's findings to another organisation without first obtaining the permission of the relevant parties to the first study.

2.   Principle of Exchange

2.1   Be willing to provide the same type and level of information that you request from your benchmarking partner to your benchmarking partner.

2.2   Communicate fully and early in the relationship to clarify expectations, avoid misunderstandings and establish mutual interest in the benchmarking exchange.

2.3   Be honest and complete.

3.   Principle of Confidentiality

3.1   Treat all benchmarking communications as confidential to the individuals and organisations concerned. Information should not be communicated outside your benchmarking partner's organisation without their prior consent.

3.2   An organisation's participation in a benchmarking study is confidential and should not be communicated externally without their permission.

4. Principle of Use

4.1   Use information obtained through benchmarking only for the purposes of improving organisational performance.

4.2   The use or communication of a benchmarking partner's name with any data obtained or practices observed requires the prior permission of that partner.

5. Principle of First Party Contact

5.1   Initiate benchmarking contacts through appropriate benchmarking contact person designated by the partner organisation.

5.2   Respect the culture and ways of working of your benchmarking partner's organisation, and work within mutually agreed procedures.

6. Principle of Third Party Contact

6.1   Obtain an individual's permission before providing his or her name in response to a contact request.

6.2   Avoid communicating a contact's name in an open forum without the contact's prior permission.

7. Principle of Preparation

7.1   Demonstrate commitment to the efficiency and effectiveness of benchmarking by being prepared prior to making an initial benchmarking contact.

7.2   Make the most of your benchmarking partner's time by being fully prepared for each exchange.

7.3   Help your benchmarking partner prepare by providing them with a questionnaire and agenda prior to benchmarking visits.

8. Principle of Completion

8.1   Follow through with each commitment made to your benchmarking partner in a timely manner.

8.2   Complete each benchmarking study to the satisfaction of all benchmarking partners as mutually agreed.

9.   Principle of Understanding and Action

9.1   Understand how your benchmarking partner would like to be treated.

9.2   Treat your benchmarking partner in the way that your benchmarking partner would want to be treated.

9.3   Understand how your benchmarking partner would like to have the information he or she has provided handled and used, and handle and use it in that manner.

Benchmarking Protocol

1.   Know and abide by the benchmarking Code of Conduct.

2.   Have a basic knowledge of benchmarking and follow a benchmarking process.

3.   Prior to initiating contact with potential benchmarking partners, have determined what to benchmark, define the process to be benchmarked, and identify the data required.

4.   Have developed a questionnaire and interview guide, and be prepared to share these in advance if requested.

5.   Possess the authority to share and be willing to share information with benchmarking partners.

6.   Work through a specified contact, and mutually agree on working and meeting arrangements.

Protocol for Benchmarking Visits

1.   Provide meeting agenda in advance.

2.   Be professional, honest, courteous and prompt.

3.   Introduce all attendees and explain why they are present.

4.   Adhere to the agenda.

5.   Use language that is universal, and not one's own jargon.

6.   Be sure that neither partner is sharing proprietary information unless prior approval has been obtained by both parties, from the proper authority.

7.   Share information about your own process, and if asked, consider sharing study results.

8. Offer to facilitate a future reciprocal visit.

9. Conclude meetings and visits on schedule.

10. Thank your benchmarking partner for sharing their process.

Benchmarking Clubs

Benchmarking clubs are self-help groups that meet firstly to agree a common understanding of the benchmarking approach and secondly to share experience, skills and possibly staff and resources. In time they may become the basis of a new form of consortium commissioning projects and supply of services. Prior to the introduction of the internal market there was an ethos of sharing and growing together. Sadly in many areas the sense of competition has made organisations wary of sharing. The club provides an opportunity to talk honestly and openly about performance, business planning, the development of business cases and purchaser relationships. The clubs therefore tend to involve members who are not in direct competition and are therefore some distance apart. Because of this the agenda and actions of the club must be focused and action orientated. Club members should learn to be organisationally generous and personally selfish or they will become frustrated. A key rule is that the member who is hungry for better practice should do the work as they have the incentive to learn.

The NHS Benchmarking Reference Centre has produced a guide on benchmarking clubs which spells out good practice in identifying partners, planning and managing a club and how to achieve results (NHSBRC, 1992d).

One of the first NHS benchmarking clubs included:

- Bradford Hospitals NHS Trust
- Glan Clwyd DHS NHS Trust
- Glan Hafren NHS Trust
- Morriston Terforys Hospital (now NHS Trust)
- Southport and Formby NHS Trust
- Swindon and Marlborough Hospital Unit (now NHS Trust)

The club has adopted the following rules:

Nominated contact: It does not matter who initiates the enquiry, it should always be through the identified point of contact;

Information is shared by consent between members, so they can control the flow of information;

Confidentiality between club members is essential unless agreed otherwise;

Honesty – you need to put your hand up for both good and bad performance.

Why do members join? Jonathan Parry, Chief Executive of Southport and Formby explains that they joined for the following reasons (Parry and Chew, 1993):

To be the Best
We have a duty as health service managers to make our organisations the best. There will always be someone better.

An Essential Part of the Quality Armoury
We support adherence to and exceed the *Patient's Charter* requirements. Our standards are ahead of the *Patient's Charter* and we can influence this process.

Analytical Tools
It is interesting to find out why someone performs better and actively compare against these organisations using process-mapping and analysing and understanding what the organisation does.

Comparative Up-to-date Information
There have been complaints that up-to-date comparative information does not exist. The reality is that we will be losing 2–3% of revenue and will be required to make a further 2% in cost savings. We cannot *afford* to say that we are all different. The information is there if you want it. If you are not pursuing up-to-date relevant information then you have no business managing your organisations. You must actively seek information and use this to pursue high quality and cost-effective care.

Contestability
There will be market-testing of services by Commissioners focusing on cost, quality and access. You must be able to demonstrate why and how you can respond to these requirements – if you cannot, then you're in trouble.

Lessons from Outside the NHS
These comparisons are not restricted by the competitive environment which has increased in the NHS. These organisations can help and like helping.

The club has adopted the framework of the NHS Wales High Level Indicators and extended them to their own purposes. Three activity levels are identified; high level indicators, second level indicators and benchmarking projects.

High Level Indicators

The high level indicators were not original to the Club. They are based on the work carried out by a joint NHS Wales Working Group. The group developed a range of HLIs covering commissioner/purchaser, provider and primary care settings (HLI, 1992).

As the club is made up of provider units, they focused on the provider HLIs and refined the list of about 100 indicators to 55.

HLIs have to be meaningful and measurable, must be able to focus on achievement/performance in-year and are intended primarily for the use of executive boards. They provide indicators in the areas of:

- activity
- efficiency
- finance
- quality.

The HLIs are provided by each member annually to allow member organisations to gauge the corporate position of each other on an annual basis thus forming a basis for comparison.

Some Examples of Club HLIs

Activity

- Number of consultant episodes
- Number of day cases
- % of bed occupancy
- Average length of stay
- Ratio: follow-up to new outpatient attendances

Efficiency

- Day cases as a % of all inpatients and day cases
- Number of cancelled planned theatre sessions
- % of elective operations cancelled twice
- Number of patients waiting more than 3 months for first outpatient appointment
- Days lost to sickness and absence as a % of total working days available

Quality

- % of complaints receiving a full written explanation of apology within 1 calender month
- Number of patients who have their operations cancelled on the day of the operation
- Number of patients not admitted within 1 month when elective operation has been cancelled twice
- % of outpatients given individual appointment times
- % of patients seen within 30 minutes of specific appointment time

Finance

- Overtime costs as a % of total pay budget
- Management costs as a % of total income
- Financial target performance
- Capital spend as a % against profile
- Debtors days
- Trade creditors days

In summary, HLIs allows a corporate view of member hospitals and assists in separating the poor performers from the good performers. More importantly, it allows members to ensure that we are not the poor performer in the club. The narrative provided with HLIs would provide the overview of changes in internal and external environment and the HLIs would help identify any shifts, or not as the case may be, to those changes.

Second Level Indicators

Second level indicators are more specific. They are aimed at specialty level and focus on inpatient, day case and outpatient activities in related specialities through activity, quality and financial indicators.

Second level indicators could be used to support local decision making and corporate performance, and are meant to be used by senior managers and managers at directorate level. All club members subscribe to the CHKS National Comparative Database of Patient Episodes (in Wales the WHICH project) which provides an additional source of detailed comparative data.

The work on second level indicators is developing and includes the following areas of interest:

- Audit Commission basket of procedures
- Outpatient procedures by specialty
- Inpatient and outpatient activity by specialty

- Empirical data on *Patient's Charter* performance by specialty procedure costs
- Fundholding GP tariffs.

The second level indicators are more specific indicators at the specialty level, focusing on inpatients, outpatients and day cases. They are intended to support local decision-making and operational management. They may also be used in support of the executive level. All benchmarking club members are collecting these second level indicators.

Benchmarking Projects

The club has also identified some projects from the *second level indicators*.

Club projects address common areas of concern and are undertaken by two members or more; most if not all of the members are usually involved. Specific projects identified within the club are:

- Sickness and absence management
- Theatre utilisation
- Orthopaedic waiting list management
- Bed management
- Drug utilisation.

These all have a club member identified as the lead.

Ad Hoc Projects have been developed as projects on request. They are led by managers at directorate level in order to increase market share and achieve improvements. These include:

- Pathology tariffs
- Organisation of acute medicine and care of the elderly
- Community midwives travelling budgets trying to identify costs of midwifery
- Gynaecology day care and outpatient procedures.

Benchmarking is recognised as a cyclical process. The club has introduced improvements and are continuing to benchmark. Members believe they 'will continue to grow and develop with benchmarking and we are looking forward to reaping the benefits of belonging to such a club. We are striving to be the best' (Parry and Chew, 1993).

Common Interest Groups

A variation on the idea of the club is the common interest group where organisations with common problems meet and agree a programme of activity around a specific issue. CIGs in health exist or are being formed for pathology, radiology, pharmacy, medical physics and community dentistry. All industry CIGs exist or are being formed for customer satisfaction, supply chain, marketing and sales order process, management information systems, business planning and strategy, new product/service introduction, utilities and human resources (The Benchmarking Centre, 1994).

The first task of these groups is usually to clarify their focus of interest and then identify members' relative performance levels. The groups may well conclude like the benchmarking clubs that they do not have best practice examples within their numbers but they will cooperate in identification of performance measure definition, best practice and project design.

Benchmarking clubs and CIGs are a powerful means of establishing a benchmarking project and sustaining momentum but they can deteriorate into talking shops if there is not a clear focus on achievement.

Benchmarking Visits

The first lesson to learn when planning a visit to look at someone else's best practice is *don't go*.

It is too easy to read about a good idea in a professional magazine, ring the author and then leap in the car to visit the site. It is unlikely that you will bring much back. You will have an interesting time, a tour of the facility but you are likely to leave overawed by the hosts performance with no idea how that performance is achieved or how to implement change back in your own organisation. The NHS Benchmarking Reference Centre have produced a guide on benchmarking visits which spells out good practice in planning, undertaking and following through on visits (NHSBRC, 1992e) and the protocol of actions from that guide is included here with the code of conduct section.

The most important stage is planning the visit based upon an understanding of your own organisation and the particular failure points you are trying to overcome. If you have carried out even the briefest process mapping of your own activity you will be able to provide your host with an explanation of your process and the problems you are facing. You should be prepared to explain why you feel they are a good practice site and be willing to share with them the information you expect them to share with you.

Your own research should have highlighted a series of questions that you wish answered and these should be prepared, piloted locally, ie can you answer them, and then sent to the host organisation in advance of the visit. For example, Ethicom Ltd, the suture manufacturers, have developed an approach which involves preparation of:

- An outline focus of the planned visit, eg we wish to look at the company wide approach and then focus on internal departments.
- A list of the questions we propose to ask.
- A copy of our benchmarking project definition.
- Definitions of terms.

This kind of approach will assist in ensuring you get to see the right people, the process owners who really know the activity and can demonstrate its effectiveness. It also allows the host to see you are serious and to judge if they really have something to offer. You may save yourself the trouble of the trip if they write back and say they would like to be benchmarking associates seeking best practice as you obviously are futher along than they are.

At the site concentrate on the performance gap between your own activity and that of the host. Record differences in process and processes which appear to be missing altogether. Remember to leave time to discuss how any recent changes were implemented. Seek to learn from mistakes as well as successes.

It is often asked why best practice organisations should bother to entertain you. There are many reasons for this. The NHS and other public services has much goodwill available to it from industry but if you waste everyones time by being ill-prepared the doors will begin to close. The kind of planning described will convince the host that you are worth engaging with and they are likely to want to continue the relationship with your organisation in areas where they are pursuing best practice. You will often find that you are explaining the benefits of benchmarking and your experience however slight will be of value to them.

Be prepared to be flexible when you arrive at the site. It is important to stick to the main objective but your approach may need to be modified. CIG Gas Cylinders of Sydney sent teams over to the UK to benchmark production of aluminium cylinders. They examined their own process strengths and weaknesses by reviewing data from their plant including rejects, productivity, downtime, housekeeping standards and quality and flowcharted the normal operation process. Key focus areas for each team member had been assigned prior to leaving Australia, but on arrival they found the difference in the UK plants so vast that they were unable to maintain such a focus and decided to review the plant together and then pool impressions. They also found that they could not stick to traditional measures such as rejects to fairly compare plants, the standards varied so widely that they had to invent new measures of quality to benchmark the plant. This the manufacturing manager reported 'ensured we couldn't pretend we were doing better than we really were' (McBurney, 1993).

Pacific Bell recently carried out a successful study on customer satisfaction without visiting anyone. Their approach to benchmarking enquiries reflects their enthusiasm for their own industry. They make phone calls, not site visits, and found their attention to planning and preparation together with their willingness to share their own system up front worked well in achieving partner cooperation (Pozos, 1993). When they were ready to talk to other companies they followed these steps:

- senior manager made initial contact with companies and identified appropriate contact;
- team members called partner companies and arranged to mail materials about project;
- team members scheduled a phone interview to ask qualitative questions. Answers were mailed back;
- two hour interviews were tape recorded. They did not make site visits.

Partners were found to be very cooperative. They answered almost all questions and provided copies of questionnaires. The next stage was for the Pacific Bell team to meet in two all-day sessions to compile findings and compare companies. They produced similarity and key difference charts comparing Pacific Bell to all other companies and managed to find a number of innovations and opportunities for cost reduction.

Finally you should be prepared to share your study results with your partners. Follow the code of conduct in presenting details if more than one partner is involved.

Comparative Data

Effective benchmarking practices depend on accurate measurement of organisational outcomes linked to identifiable processes. These measurements can then highlight comparable processes from other organisations. There have been many attempts to establish performance indicators, key statistical indicators etc in health and other sectors but they have often failed to meet the needs of both policy review and operational management.

This section looks at some developments in health-care services overseas and attempts in the UK to establish meaningful performance measures which support operational management and best practice comparison. Two initiatives in NHS Wales are described, the rationalisation of data collection within high level indicators and making available of patient episode data in a form which encourages comparison with best in class performers.

USA Developments

The Joint Commission on Accreditation of Health-care organisations in the US recently established a data system designed to allow organisations to access comparative measures of outcomes and processes. The system includes the development and extensive testing of performance measures. The Commission intends to utilise the data to identify and study organisations with the best outcomes and to provide the results of these studies to other organisations to aid in their process development. The Joint Commission realised the need for the indicators to be based upon practical operational need and to have wide consensus. They therefore embarked on a comprehensive programme of alpha testing to confirm validity, reliability and collectability and beta testing to give users the opportunity to provide feedback on the usefulness and costs of collection. The staging of the programme covers:

1. anaesthesia, obstetrics;
2. trauma, oncology, cardiovascular;
3. medication use, infection control;
4. home infusion therapy;
5. depression;
6. perioperative care.

The plan is for participating organisations to provide 10 indicators in each subject area on a voluntary basis in 1994, 20 indicators in 1995 and 30 indicators within a revised accreditation plan in 1996.

The NHS in Wales has adopted the development approach used by the Joint Commission and in particular the style of presentation of indicators during development. Each indicator has clearly expressed the definition, rationale and formula of the indicator.

The Mission of the Joint Commission on Accreditation of Health-care organisations is to improve the quality of health-care provided to the public. The Joint Commission develops standards of quality in collaboration with health professionals and others and stimulates health-care organisations to meet or exceed the standards through accreditation and teaching of quality improvement concepts (JCAHO, 1992).

High Level Indicators

The NHS in Wales embarked on a set of high level indicator (HLI) monitoring in 1991. The first year was solely concerned with acute provider units. The second year extended this to commissioners, primary care and other providers and the third year (94/95) has restructured the indicators to take account of the more modest requirements of central departments.

The process has been led by service chief executives at NHS Directorate (now Welsh Office Health Department) invitation with the intention to extend the approach to cover all NHS organisations in Wales and if possible further afield to which end it has been shared with the NHS Management Executive and the Audit Commission.

The indicators support:

- DHAs and FHSAs in monitoring their own commissioning performance and internal management performance.

- Unit management boards and trusts in monitoring their own provider performance, whether they are involved in the provision of secondary, community or primary care services.

- FHSAs in the measurement of their responsibility for primary care provider performance.

- The monitoring requirements of the NHS directorate by providing a first stage assessment for the annual review of health commissioners.

The indicators have been developed to assist judgement of 'business' performance following the principles that the indicators should be derived from operational management, be meaningful, measurable and cost-effective to collect. They should be capable of being used by executive boards and the NHS directorate to focus on achievements in-year. The indicators are also important to enable decision-makers to identify where further investigatory work may be necessary to provide reassurance to the users of the service that quality and cost-effectiveness are being delivered.

The main criteria for determining whether an indicator is high level or not are:

- Does it satisfy management board requirements?

- Does it respond to central information needs?

- Is it useful for comparative information?

One of the advantages of the HLI approach has been the integration of indicators from different areas of activity. Traditionally hospital management has reviewed activity, finance and personnel as separate issues involving different groups of staff and a different basis of data collection and monitoring. With the development of clinical directorates and service business managers it has been clear that these areas must be integrated. The HLI approach allows performance to be reviewed on the basis of the whole rather than elements of the organisation's performance. The intention then is that performance should be reviewed on an exception basis, with non-achievement and over-achievement clearly identified and reported against planned levels. The summary of these key principles is set out below:

- Draw together and integrate management information.
- Measure the essential features of activity that directly contribute to the success or otherwise of the organisation.
- Focus on normal business.
- Provide for exception reporting based on local targets.
- Be timely, relevant and provide the basis for future management action.
- Provide easy to interpret information which executive and non-executive directors find acceptable.

The progress of this initiative is outlined below.

High Level Indicators: Progress

1991/2   Basic approach introduced concentrating on provider performance.

Introduced into Annual Review process.

1992/3   Approach developed to embrace:
commissioners;
secondary care providers;
primary care providers;
community health service providers;
More sophisticated monitoring format.

Established as component of Annual Review process.
Integration of returns, eg *Patient Charter*/waiting times.

1993/4   Approach consolidated and refined:
new ambulance and psychiatric care services indicators;
refined primary/community indicators.
Central Information Review to reduce numbers of required statistical returns.
Distribution of PC-based data collection and reporting system (HLIS).

1994/5   Further refinement of the system, fewer indicators.
Introduction of opt-in middle level indicators.

The format for the supporting documentation to the indicators is given below (VFM, 1992e).

High Level Indicator:
Definition of Terms:
Rationale for Indicators:
Indicator Calculations: Numerator Denominator Indicator Rate = Numerator/Denominator Indicator % = Numerator/Denominator × 100

The data is collected quarterly onto a PC-based system (HLIS) which requires some initial setting up by the local commissioner or hospital. The hospital for example should establish local targets internally or with their providers or fundholding GPs and plan the likely profile of performance for the four quarters. This allows for the kind of variation usually experienced due to seasonal factors, contracting requirements or new facilities becoming available. The quarterly data is then added to the system which highlights variation from the local and all Wales targets and confirms if performance is outside agreed tolerance levels. The system allows organisations to load comparative data which can be best performance, all Wales Average, Benchmarking Club or Peer Group comparison or the last year's performance of the unit.

The system is part of the formal monitoring framework for the NHS in Wales but has obvious application for other organisations seeking to reform their standard performance monitoring. In addition the system allows organisations or benchmarking clubs to set and compare their sets of indicators for example at department or specialty level. These 'middle level indicators are now being developed using the same definition-rationale-formula approach described above (see Figures 3.1–3.3).

Patient Episode Database

The high level indicators provide aggregate data and together with the development of middle level or departmental indicators go some way to fill a gap which frustrates benchmarking initiatives. However there is also a need for a more comprehensive database of clinical activity. In

Service Description	User/Client Profile	Purchaser	Influencers	Contract Currency
CHILD HEALTH SERVICES: Consultant-led Child Health Service for pre-school children. Safety-net clinics provided to complement and supplement services provided by family doctor. Will include specialist medical, nursing and therapeutic services to children with special needs.	Pre-school children (0–4 years); expectant and nursing mothers	DHA	Family doctors; health visitors; primary health care teams; district nursing service; social services; education dept.; community midwives; other professionals	
School Age Children Comprehensive school health service for all children in schools maintained by the Local Education Authority, including specialist medical, nursing and therapeutic services for children identified as having special needs following assessment under provisions of 1981 Education Act.	School age children (5–16 years); parents; headmaster	DHA	Headteachers; school nurses; named doctor and nurse allocated to school; education authority; social services; adoption agency; social workers; community homes	
Dental Services for Children A dental health service for children, including preventative, screening and treatment services.	Pre-school and school children with special needs/in area of social deprivation	DHA	Teachers; healthcare professionals	
Child Protection Child protection service, provided alongside Child health and School health provision, including Health Visiting, medical and administrative back-up services. Monitoring families and children 'at risk' or 'potentially at risk' of child abuse and following up actual cases of child abuse.	Pre-school and school children 'at risk'; families 'at risk'	DHA/Social Services	Health Visitors; social services dept; Police; NSPCC; family doctor	

FIG. 3.1

Service Description	User/Client Profile	Purchaser	Influencers	Contract Currency
ADULT SERVICES				
District Nursing Skilled nursing care to patients during the acute phase of their illness to enable them to remain in their homes, avoiding unnecessary admission to hospital and to facilitate early discharge.	Acutely ill adult	DHA	?	District Nursing Treatments (service level)
Skilled nursing care to patients during their treatment, post operative or palliative care phase of their illness	Patients with cancers and malignant diseases	DHA	?	
Comprehensive nursing care and support to terminally ill patients in community settings during the terminal illness phase leading to a peaceful death.	Terminal care patients and bereaved	DHA	?	
Skilled nursing care when required to enable patients to remain in their homes, avoiding unnecessary admission to hospital or other institutional care. Provide continuity of nursing care following discharge from hospital. Comprehensive service based on the care needs of the individual and family/carer.	Chronically sick or physically disabled	DHA	Other agencies	
Skilled nursing care to frail, sick, disabled and terminally ill patients to enable them to remain in their own homes avoiding unnecessary admission to hospital and other institutional care and to facilitate early discharge from hospital. Comprehensive service based on the assessment and needs of the carer.	Elderly	DHA	Social services; GPs; caring agencies	

FIG. 3.2

Service Description	User/Client Profile	Purchaser	Influencers	Contract Currency
CHILDRENS HEALTH SERVICES Provide multidisciplinary service for the assessment and treatment of children, to ensure they reach maximum potential. To promote the health of pre-school and school age children in order to ensure a healthy adult population in the future. To identify developmental and sensory delay at the earliest possible age. Ensure required treatment and support including referral to the Education department for children with special educational needs. To work with other agencies for the protection of children, working with their families, and those children looked after by the Social Services Department or other agencies. To achieve and sustain vaccination and immunisation targets to work towards the elimination of preventable childhood infections and their possible consequences. To provide the necessary health-care support to children in need because of a disability to enable them to lead as independent a life as possible.	Pre-school children; school children; children 'at risk'	DHA; education dept.; social services	Family practitioners; social services; education authority; voluntary organisations;	Immunisation – completed Courses (%) – range Childhood surveillance: 6 weeks medical and developmental examination. 9 month medical and developmental examination. 18 month Denver test. 8 month hearing screening test. 3.5 year orthoptic screening. Nursery audiometry. School Entry medicals. Audiometric Screening (Age 6). Vision Screening (5/8/11/14). Service Contracts/Treatments: Health Visitor contacts; District nurse treatments; Physiotherapy treatments; Occupational therapy treatments; Speech Therapy treatments; Pyschology treatments; Chiropody treatments; Audiology clinic attendances; Eye clinic attendances; Orthoptic clinic attendances; App D medical. Detailed medical developmental assessment. Dental treatment contacts. Dental treatment episodes. Dental health promotion contacts. Dental screening contacts.

FIG. 3.3

Wales the Patient Episode Database for Wales (PEDW) already in theory provided a pool of data for research, monitoring and clinical audit. In practice like many large centralised databases the system was flawed with only some of the data getting from hospital records to local and/or district information departments and the central processing office in Cardiff.

Those who did manage to abstract and send their data were rewarded with masses of error slips for records which failed validation routines. In practice the system did not work and was in danger of floundering as a system at all. This was beginning to be compounded by the creation of trust status for hospitals who were becoming concerned at their data being processed by district information departments.

In 1992 NHS Wales signed an agreement on behalf of all its acute units with a private information service organisation, CHKS. The contract to run initially for three years was established to process abstracts of the PEDW database to provide quality and comparative database reports to hospitals as part of the benchmarking initiative. This is called the Welsh Health Information for the Comparison of Hospitals (WHICH) project.

The project went to some pains to involve the hospitals as users rather than contributors to the system. Although the initiative was funded by the Welsh Office to April 1995, each hospital has agreed to sign up to a service level agreement which sets out as a contract of understanding the responsibilities of each party involved. This also covers issues of confidentiality and the principles of the benchmarking code of conduct.

For each hospital the PEDW data abstract is processed monthly and individual records which have been coded in the hospital to ICD-9 diagnostic codes are calibrated and grouped to the DRG classification. A monthly report is produced to highlight issues of data quality and comparative performance. A PC-based software system provides for local interrogation of the information against a peer group of similar hospitals. The hospital can be graded for the quality of its data to allow units to have confidence that the comparisons are valid.

Comparative analysis reports are available by hospital/specialty covering:

- Activity summary
- Bed day utilisation
- Waiting lists
- Length of stay
- Day cases
- Quality indicators

- Admission/discharge profiles
- Coding quality analysis.

The example in fig. 3.5 shows how the information can be used.

The system is being developed and extended to more hospitals in the UK and overseas with hospitals in France and Spain already joining and sharing information as part of benchmarking initiatives. A similar project is intended to be developed with community health services and commissioning organisations.

In both of these initiatives, HLIs and WHICH, there was some early scepticism that the projects simply involved more centralised data gathering and for some this may still become a self-fulfilling prophecy if no use is made of the data. However both projects have a number of characteristics which have contributed to their success.

The initiatives were prompted to encourage use of the data and involved participants who were not committed to the old systems and structures.

Both projects have strong project management elements built into them to set up and to maintain the initiative. The projects also follow the resource management principles set out in the *Information and Information Technology Strategic Direction* (Welsh Office, 1989c):

- commitment
- timely feedback
- involvement of those who generate the data
- confidence in the accuracy of data
- cost-effective collection
- derived from operational systems
- stability and improvement.

The last point concerns continual improvement in performance measurement. The HLI working team reporting in 1992/3 sought to establish the principle that the indicators should be 'held' for two years to allow the system to become established. The Joint Commission work in the USA recognised this point and sought to establish indicators which would last several years although the level of acceptable performance targets might change (JCAHO, 1992). In practice this has not proven possible with all the indicators, however the approach has stabilised and the number of other returns have been dramatically cut.

Unfortunately at present the performance indicator sets for England, Scotland and Northern Ireland are different. The next challenge will be to seek to integrate the data definitions across UK and international boundaries and between public services and industry.

		Provider High Level Indicators	Welsh Office Core Indicators	All-Wales Target	Local Target	Actual Position	Actual Variance	% Variance	Direction or tolerance level	Tick if within tolerance ✓ x
6.	Q	Number of patients who have their operation cancelled on the day of the operation	N						+10%	
7.	Q	Number of operations carried out between midnight and 8.00 a.m.	N						+50%	
8.	Q	% of inpatients occupying a hospital bed solely due to the non-availability of the required continuing health or social care (excluding community hospitals)	Y	Q					+50%	
9.	Q	Number of day cases	Y	Q					+10%	
10.	Q	Day cases as a % of all day cases and elective inpatients	N						−5%	
11.	Q	Unplanned Readmissions	Y	Q						
12.	Q	Invection Rates	Y	Q						
13.	Q	Number of new outpatients	Y	Q					−5% to +5%	
14.	Q	New outpatients as a % of all referrals	Y	Q					−5% to +5%	
15.	Q	Ratio: follow up to new outpatient attendances	N	Q					−5% to +5%	

FIG. 3.4   Example HLIs

	Hospital	%	Peer	%
Total Episodes	37875		559844	
Invalid Diagnosis Codes(s)	68	0.18	18042	3.22
Date of Birth conflict with Dates	7	0.02	288	0.05
Inappropriate Primary Dx (excluding uncoded)	90	0.24	9315	1.66
E-Code is Primary	14	0.04	103	0.02
Manifestation Code is Primary	37	0.10	0	0.00
Primary Dx also Secondary	5	0.01	714	0.13
Start and End Date Errors	0	0.00	2160	0.39
Provider Spell End Date Missing	1069	2.82	8509	1.52
Questionable Admission	356	0.94	3999	0.71
Diagnosis conflict with Sex	2	0.01	458	0.08
Diagnosis conflict with Age	4	0.01	1334	0.24
Primary Diagnosis is Non-specific	6473	17.09	102695	18.34
Procedure is Non-specific	15268	40.31	48910	8.74
Inappropriate Diagnosis for Procedure	437	1.15	7393	1.32
Procedure Code(s) Invalid	11	0.03	1788	0.32
Procedure conflict with Sex	3	0.01	56	0.01
Procedure conflict with Age	0	0.00	0	0.00
Primary Procedure without Dx	13	0.03	518	0.09
V-Code Diagnoses present	8754	23.11	129510	23.13
E-Code Diagnoses present	2656	7.01	37427	6.69
Episode with 0 Diagnoses Recorded	17	0.04	31556	5.64
Episode with 1 Diagnosis Recorded	16916	44.66	259464	46.35
Episode with 2 Diagnoses Recorded	11740	31.00	158251	28.27
Episode with 3 Diagnoses Recorded	5295	13.98	64504	11.52
Episode with 4 Diagnoses Recorded	2292	6.05	25902	4.63
Episode with 5 Diagnoses Recorded	973	2.57	12154	2.17
Episode with 6 Diagnoses Recorded	642	1.70	7611	1.36
Episode with 7 Diagnoses Recorded	0	0.00	395	0.07
Average No of Dx for Coded Episodes	1.96		1.86	

Quality data is essential if projects are to produce valid and repeatable results.

Diagnostic coding and use of supplementary codes are good here. Use of procedure codes is less accurate.

Coders and clinicians can work together to continually improve the richness of data that coding systems offer.

In-depth coding at this stage can supplement audit systems installed at departmental level.

FIG 3.5

Total Bed Days by Length of Stay	Bed Days	%	Peer Bed Days	%
Total Bed Days	41327		4283132	
Intended Day Cases LOS > 0	508	1.23	25421	0.59
1 or 2 Days	5188	12.55	371179	8.67
Between 3–4 Days	5434	13.15	369186	8.62
Between 5–7 Days	7715	18.67	515675	12.04
Between 8–14 Days	9553	23.12	836888	19.54
Between 15–28 Days	7703	18.64	783380	18.29
Between 29–49 Days	3628	8.78	485798	11.34
Over 49 Days	2106	5.10	921041	21.50

This table gives a useful overview of bed utilisation over a six month period. Twice as many patients are admitted as intended day cases as in the peer group. However, a large percentage of these appear to have overnight stays after all.

Lengths of stay are higher overall than the peer group. However, longer stays (+28 days) appear to be catered for elsewhere. What does this mean for contracting? This data could serve as a prompt to review length of stay across each specialty or within chosen DRGs.

FIG 3.6

Hospital Details	Hospital	%	Peer	%
Total Admissions	10661		836384	
Male Patients	4552	42.70	360508	43.10
Female Patients	6109	57.30	475773	56.88
Admissions (exc OB/NB)	9101	85.37	724674	86.64
Number of Patients of Age >75	1618	15.18	112629	13.47
Number of Patients of Age <16	2005	18.81	139803	16.72
Average Patient Age	44		43	
Average Patient Age (excl OB/NB)	49		47	
Elective Admissions	4722	44.29	410199	49.04
Emergency Admissions	4281	40.16	303369	36.27
Admissions from other NHS Provider	98	0.92	11106	1.33
Discharge on Clinical Advice	10367	97.33	813749	97.11
Self Discharge	48	0.45	4271	0.51
Died	232	2.18	19027	2.27
Stillbirth	2	0.02	115	0.01
Other Discharge	2	0.02	784	0.09
Total Discharges	10651		837946	

An easy-to-view hospital profile. Higher proportions of elderly patients and children may have resource implications. The split between emergency and elective work does not compare well with the peer group and may be prejudicial to this hospital's financial position.

Some hospitals have used the database to begin to review GP referral patterns. In this way, they can learn what GPs are looking for in a local hospital service, offer a responsive service, and better manage the demand on beds.

FIG 3.7

Maturity Matrices and Good Practice/Resource Releasing Guides

Maturity Matrices

Maturity matrices are grids identifying the range of performance for a number of elements within a key issue. A simple commercial example could be processing of book or component orders.

Issue: Order Processing	Below Minimum	Minimum Standard	Good Practice	Best Practice
TOS (temp. out of stock)	>5%	<5%	<1%	None after June 1994
Time to dispatch	Months	Weeks	Days	Hours

FIG. 3.8

The advantages of this approach are:

- The guides are supportive rather than prescriptive.
- The approach supports both self-assessment and simple external review.
- The approach clarifies minimum standards which are required, good practice which can be achieved and best practice to which health-care may aspire if resources and priorities allow.
- The approach is outward looking, building on the best from health-care and industry throughout UK and overseas.
- The approach promotes the principles of managers releasing resources to achieve priorities rather than always seeking new resources.
- The guides are generally descriptive allowing easy recognition and placing of local circumstances within the grids, however where high or middle level indicators are available these can be included, where they are not they can be developed.

The following example deals with a number of elements of patient discharge from acute hospital: It is relatively easy to assess from this matrix the current arrangements and also to see where the units performance is unbalanced, for example great efforts may have been made to organise external coordination of care, but internal discharge arrangements are still below minimum, consequently all parties are

105

frustrated. Conversely improving discharge to within 30 mins of consultant advice may be too fast for social services to activate necessary support in the home.

This example is illustrative only, in fact where best practice is not known or an example cannot be quoted it would be better to say this rather than encourage resources to be expended trying to achieve spurious levels of performance.

Issue: Discharge from hospital				
Elements	Below Minimum	Minimum Standard	Good Practice	Best Practice
Patient discharged	no coordination of ward rounds, med recs, pharmacy or PTS; patients freq stay extra night	Patient discharged on day of consultants advice	Patient medical records, drugs and PTS planned to allow discharge within 2 hours of advice	Patient discharged within 30 mins of consultants advice
Community care plan organised	Discharge and approp agencies informed	Approp agencies involved in discharge decision	Availability of coordinated care package options known	Tailored care packages negotiated with patient, relatives and GP
Discharge Letters	Not issued	GP to receive within 21 days of discharge	GP receives within 2 days of discharge	GP recs notice of admission, extension of planned length of stay and discharge within 12 hours of event

FIG 3.9

Benchmarking and Time Management

The first stage in a benchmarking project is to identify the key issues in your organisation that need your attention. There are many issues and many ways by which these will present themselves. Unfortunately all too often it is todays presenting problems that get the attention over the persistent nags that can always wait another day and will always be there. Think about the problems you handled yesterday. Were they the big 'A' issues that must be attended to if you and your organisation are to survive successfully. Were they the 'someone elses problems' the 'B' issues that you ended up dealing with or were they the fire fighting – attending to the leaking roof 'C' problems? Benchmarking is concerned with ensuring you tackle those A problems although you might start by looking at the process failures that keep bringing you those Bs & Cs.

The sections that follow concentrate on identifying some of the persistent issues that appear time and time again in discussions with organisations, in business planning and quality reviews, in Audit reports and in customer complaints. The issues persist because so often they are not tackled systematically or the evidence of failure is not believed. Benchmarking provides a mechanism for realisation, prioritisation and implementation of change. You will not be able to undertake this exercise alone, you must work with others. I hope you will see from this book how many other organisations face the same issues and the opportunities that exist for effective networking either by refocusing your existing professional groups or by establishing new groups that transcend artificial boundaries within your organisation and between your organisation and others.

Chapter 4
Key Issues in Health

This section looks at the key issues in health, the monitoring arrangements and existing efforts towards continuous improvement and opportunities to further adopt benchmarking.

The development of commissioning with a purchaser–provider split, GP fundholders, multi-funds and new models of service provision from NHS trusts, GPs, social services and private health-care groups has placed great strains on traditional accountability. The relationship between health authorities and government department is relatively clear as is the districts relationships with remaining directly managed units (DMVs), but NHS trusts now have many lines of accountability, all of which in Wales, ultimately end up with the Welsh Office Accounting Officer and the Secretary of State for Wales.

Each year the Welsh Office issues guidance on the current position and its plans for performance and accountability review. This has been laid out in the *Agenda for Action* and *Caring for the Future* documents but is usually supplemented by a Welsh Office circular and letter to chairman and chief executives.

In March 1993 the guidance explained the annual review process operating at three levels and concentrating on the review of progress in the top 10 management priority areas identified in *Caring for the Future*. Whilst the Annual Review meeting itself (third level) would continue to draw most attention, it was intended that most of the detailed assessment and discussion would occur at level two (bilateral meetings between officers of NHS Directorate and commissioning authorities) and first level exception reporting based upon the high level indicators.

In parallel there would be separate means of holding NHS trusts accountable.

First Level Review: High Level Performance Indicators

The indicators were designed to be used by District Health Authorities DHAs and Family Health Service Authorities FHSAs to monitor their own commissioning performance, internal management performance and the performance of DMUs. FHSAs could also use the set as a measurement of their responsibility for primary care provider performance through the practices delivering services within the FHSA area.

The indicator set provided an opportunity for authorities to report to the NHS Directorate on an exemptions basis highlighting the reasons for any substantial variances from targeted performance and standards.

Second Level Performance Reviews

It was recognised in 1992/3 that where performance appeared to be substantially above or below targeted levels there needed to be a mechanism to examine it more closely. Therefore, where necessary, a series of 'second level' meetings were held between the Welsh Office and DHA/FHSA and Community Health Councils CHC representatives to consider key issues.

The agenda and format for these meetings varied between authorities depending upon local circumstances but reviewed progress towards an integrated approach to purchasing and also monitored DMU performance. The Welsh Office also reviewed with joint county planning teams of social services, health authorities and their partners, performance under the all Wales mental handicap and mental illness strategies and implementation of the 'Caring for People' community care reforms.

Third Level: Annual Review Meeting – Agenda

The 'third level' meeting of the Annual Review was an opportunity to take stock of any major variations from plan performance in the previous financial year and to identify the key challenges for medium term. It was set against the backcloth of the HLI information and the feedback from the second level meetings. The appropriate director of social services was invited to attend in the interests of encouraging joint working and partnership. In 1994 the reviews will be chaired by Ministers.

NHS Trusts

NHS trusts are formally accountable to their board of executive directors and are held accountable through review of their financial performance and adherence to strategic and operational plans. Commissioning authorities including GP fundholders influence their providers performance through the mechanism of contracts. The first years of contracting have been based upon crude block contracts with increasing sophistication moving to cost and volume, health gain and DRG-based contracts. Directly managed units and internal services are usually managed through service level agreements (SLAs). In practice all parts of the NHS are the same organisation and the Secretary of State cannot have a contract with him/herself. All NHS 'contracts' are therefore contracts of understanding.

Because of this there has been much debate about the relationship between providers and purchasers and where the balance of power lies. Many areas seemed to be emulating the birth of the universe with the distance between providers and their old health authority increasing exponentially.

Commissioning (including Public Health Medicine & Contracting)

> *Key Issues*
>
> - Purchaser/Provider relationships
> - Needs assessment
> - Prioritisation
> - Contracting process
> - Role for public health medicine
> - Information provision
> - Joint commissioning
> - GP fundholders
> - Waiting list management
> - Extra-contractual referrals
> - Measuring clinical effectiveness
> - The cost of commissioning

1. Purchaser/Provider Relationships

In some areas purchaser/provider relationships are clearly strained and the need exists to foster a spirit of partnership and common understanding rather than one of confrontation and adversarial negotiation. However the government is wary of cosy relationships. 'In some ways we have not yet seen enough tension between trusts and purchasers ... One of the outcomes of purchasers becoming stronger will be more disputes and differences. 'It will be more noisy. If it is never noisy, then I fear there will be a kind of coalition in which the patient will be the loser.' (Secretary of State for Health, 1994). However it is possible that relationships will improve when improvements are made to the contracting process (see below). Also there is some evidence that relationships are better with providers who are still directly managed by their health authority.

2.   Needs Assessment

This is an integral feature of the reforms but there is evidence to suggest that needs assessment is perceived as irrelevant:

> 'I leave all that health needs nonsense to public health . . . it's irrelevant . . . I just place contracts and try to get more out of them [the provider] than they are giving us at the moment.' (in Freemantle et al, 1993).

However this perception is not universal, and seems to be linked with the financial pressures in the organisation. It is true to say that needs assessment is at a very early stage everywhere and must be developed from simply an information gathering process to one which can inform purchaser decisions. It also seems needs assessment is progressing most effectively in areas where attempts have been made to forge links between other bodies that provide health services – and that the future lies with joint purchasing authorities who could move the balance of power to the primary sector. The experience of Australian and European authorities who determine service priorities on assessed needs but do not have a provider/purchaser split is likely to be interesting.

3.   Prioritisation

This remains the most intractable problem with so many influences at work. A whole raft of prioritisation, demand control, rationing, resource releasing issues emerge (see Figure 4.1):

- assessment of top down priorities (ie government targets such as reduction of waiting times);
- assessment of bottom up priorities (involvement of local people in needs assessment/prioritisation process – although it has been found difficult to do this effectively);
- professional opinion (eg involvement of GPs);
- research based evidence including clinical trials where available and economic evaluation – although there is little evidence to suggest cost effectiveness methods currently inform purchaser decisions, probably due to the lack of reliable information;
- use of other criteria (eg services for life threatening conditions requiring urgent admission, unmet need or service gap and the extent to which a disease affects the population).

A 1992 study, funded by Nuffield Provincial Hospitals Trust, suggested that faced with prioritisation of services health authorities were in general responding by spreading small amounts of extra money to as many priorities as possible. However this may not be due to an unwillingness to make difficult decisions but an attempt to be seen as meeting as many consumer and provider interests as possible. What is clear is that in the future, the pressure to prioritise services will mount – and health authorities will need to develop the tools at their disposal to be able to do the job (Klein and Redmayne, 1992).

4. Contracting Process

Issues include:

- how to make discussions more productive;
- development of an agreed timetable;
- time given to providers to respond to purchaser requirements;
- information given to purchasers by providers and vice-versa;
- clarification of services required under each contract (need for more specific contracts);
- influence over service and standards;
- development of effective contracting monitoring arrangements;
- development of contracts to accommodate changes in demand;
- clarification of risk taking;
- development of mechanisms to cope with major change.

5. Role for Public Health Medicine

Can public health medicine resist its marginalisation in the current purchaser/provider environment. Issues include:

- does public health medicine have a role to play in the commissioning process? It has been suggested that the emphasis on needs assessment runs contrary to the public health medicine ethos of improving the health of the population through disease prevention and health promotion;
- can public health medicine continue in its former role as brokers between medicine and management?
- can public health professionals keep their concerns on the purchasing agenda and encourage commissioners to refocus their priorities in the light of the social, economic and environmental factors which have a direct bearing on the health of the population.

6. Information Provision

For the internal market to function properly health authorities, hospitals and GPs will need to exchange large amounts of electronic information. Issues include:

- development of coherent and effective information strategies;
- development of local and wide area networks;
- development of protocols for access to and security of information.

7. Joint Commissioning

With GPs as well as health authorities responsible for commissioning some services on behalf of their patients, and with local authorities now responsible for buying residential services for community care, the success of the NHS reforms depend to some extent upon good inter-organisational relationships. Key ingredients to these relationships include 'a shared vision as a foundation to joint action, along with compatibility in planning and commissioning intentions'.

Benefits:
- greater flexibility and coordination across organisations;
- more effective use of available resources, reducing both overlap of services and unmet needs;
- raising of mutual awareness which should engender cooperation rather than competition.

Costs:
- the need to jointly work out complex procedures and face up to issues which may have been buried for a long time;
- the danger that one party may perceive a loss of control.

8. GP Fundholders

The creation of GP fundholders is an integral feature of the NHS reforms. Early successes have included improvements in services by some practices, more effective use of resources and the general raising of the profile of GPs. However problems still remain and issues include:
- use of fundholders to provoke effective purchasing from commissioners;
- risk of GPs in selecting some patients rather than others;
- maintenance of standards as a more diverse range of practices come into fundholding;
- the need to link fundholders into national health strategies;
- 'doubts' about whether the present level of management allowance compensate for the extra work;
- the small proportion of NHS funds the fundholders have control over (over 80% of total spend is currently in the hands of HAs);
- impact on community services – possible formation of integrated primary health-care teams;
- worries over the increased workload for GPs.

9. Waiting List Management

Towards the end of the financial year 1992–93, funding for elective surgery ran out in several health districts. Exacerbating this, the public also perceive that:

- access to services differed between patients of different GPs;
- access to services differed according to which district they lived in.

A third potential problem is that low-priority cases may be taking precedence over more serious ones as both purchasers and providers try to reduce their longest waiting patients in accordance with government guidelines.

With health authorities currently considering new approaches to prioritisation of services, waiting times and their management are going to continue as an emotive issue, as is equity of access to services. Possible further issues incude:

- restriction of elective surgery by named procedure;
- professionally managed demand for elective surgery.

10. Extra-contractual Referrals

Extra-contractual referrals have important implications for purchasing authorities – especially concerning the flexibility, choice and equity of service provision and its finance – as these referrals are paid for separately and almost always at a higher cost.

11. Measuring Clinical Effectiveness

Considerable progress has been made in refining measures of clinical outcomes but in many cases the link between buying of services and health gain is still to be proven. The main R&D agenda must continue to be focused on knowing what works combined with effective structures of clinical audit which support continual improvement in service delivery.

12. The Cost of Commissioning

What is the cost of commissioning and how and why does it vary is likely to remain the principal external focus. Recent directives have set the optimum size for health authorities. They have yet to demonstrate whether they can manage to deliver these 'smart sized' organisations and be effective commissioners.

Waiting Times

Waiting list management and achievement of patient charter standards is a shared and seemingly intractable issue for commissioners and providers. The waiting list initiative annually pumps additional monies into the system to seek to reduce the politically unacceptable long waits. In November 1991, the NHS Directorate set out to identify key issues and to seek to develop longer-term solutions for the management of waiting times across Wales (VFM, 1992f).

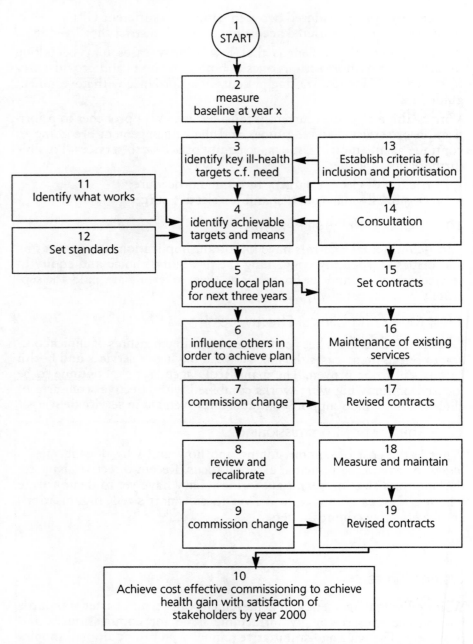

The table shows the application of first stage process mapping to Commissioner Benchmarking. The map highlights the issue that there is a need to move from maintenance of existing contracts to commissioning for health gain.

FIG. 4.1   Process Mapping for Commissioners

Acute Provider Units

Outpatient Care

Key Issues
- Waiting times
- Referrals (procedures and appointment times)
- Pre-appointment investigations
- Clinic organisation
- Patients failing to attend
- Consultants and junior staff
- Review patients
- Review after hospital discharge
- Letters to GPs
- Waiting areas and clinic facilities
- Administration
- Audit

Inpatient care

Key issues
- Admission
- Placement
- Discharge
- Bed availability and management
- Patient flow
- Length of stay
- Day surgery
- Waiting lists

The objective of the project was to produce good practice guidance on a wide spectrum of issues for the effective management of waiting lists and times.

In developing these good practice guides, considerable emphasis was placed on the active involvement of provider units and purchasers. The project team worked closely with consultants, managers and other involved personnel at nine of the largest hospitals in Wales.

Following discussions with each relevant main purchaser and detailed interviews with staff at provider units, a position statement and action plan was prepared with each hospital. These action plans were intended to form part of the contract negotiation process between purchasers and providers in Wales.

An additional spin off from the hospital visits was the development of a portfolio of case studies, principles, models and examples of successful waiting list management, which were used to confirm the selection of the 10 good practice areas and to draft the actual good practice guidelines. The content of the guides was evaluated in further discussions with hospitals in Wales, as well as individual managers and clinicians in England, and with GP fundholders.

The *Good Practice Guides* (NHS Wales 1992b) focus on a range of issues including traditional areas for study such as clinical and administrative validation, and information requirements in managing waiting lists. However, the *Guides* also address other areas such as purchaser and provider obligations in the management of waiting times and lists, and the development of more sophisticated contracts which explicitly include waiting list and waiting time performance targets.

The 10 NHS waiting times good practice guides:

WT1	*Waiting List Validation*
WT2	*Structuring the Waiting List*
WT3	*Information to/from GPs*
WT4	*Producing Purchaser Information*
WT5	*Producing Provider Information*
WT6	*Waiting Time in Contracts*
WT7	*Purchaser and Provider Obligations*
WT8	*Managing Waiting Lists*
WT9	*Managing Patient Care*
WT10	*Tender Specification and Bids*

The *Good Practice Guides* are of direct relevance to both purchasers and providers in helping them to meet more effectively their varying responsibilities in relation to waiting lists and waiting times.

Each of the 10 guides focused on specific topics, some of which will apply to all sectors of the target audience, and others to specific sections only. Each guide provides background information to the topic, identifies key elements for consideration, and describes three levels of practice: minimum, good and best practice, against each of the key elements as illustrated in fig 4.2.

KEY ELEMENTS	MINIMUM	GOOD PRACTICE	BEST PRACTICE
Day theatre use	Dedicated day theatre available	Day theatre linked to pre-operative assessment clinics	Develop day case protocols – identify patient groups for day surgery
Return outpatient appointments	Monitor return to new outpatient ratio	Develop clear criteria for discharge to GP	Develop outpatient protocols – number of and reason for return visits
Theatre Management	Emergency theatre available	Identify sessions available to be booked by consultants/specialities	Introduce three session working, theatre to be utilised over 12 hours

FIG 4.2

A specific practical application of the guides, therefore, is that they present an opportunity for purchasers and providers to assess their own position in relation to each element of each area of the good practice guidance and plan action accordingly. Areas where, for example, current practice in a hospital, or indeed at specialty level, falls below the specified minimum standard, should be a priority for improvement. The next step would then be for the hospital to plan how to move along the continuum towards best practice.

The *Good Practice Guides* can also be used as a means of enhancing the developing relationships between purchaser and provider. For these areas in particular, there are considerable benefits in planning together the steps towards best practice, such as:

- A shared agenda for action on the management of waiting lists and improvements in waiting times;
- Agreement on areas which should be priorities for investment;
- Agreement on the timescale against which specific progress should be made.

Managing Patient Flow

During the course of the project, a number of clinicians and managers suggested the guides should be developed within an overall concept of patient flow management. This would enable their most effective use and encourage greater understanding of the relationship between all the factors needing to be managed with relation to waiting times.

Managing patient flow is important for both purchasers and providers, although each will have a slightly different focus. Figure 4.3 shows a simplified representation of the surgical treatment process through which patients in a hospital might pass. This model has subsequently been used in many benchmarking initiatives in Wales as a means of focusing attention on key failure points but with a recognition of the need to look beyond the presenting problem to where the real pressure is being applied (NHS Wales 1992a).

Effective management of patient flow within provider hospitals needs to take place at whole hospital and speciality level to ensure that patients pass through the treatment process with minimum delay, and that blockage points do not occur with resultant increases in waiting times.

At specialty level this will mean, for example, monitoring referral rates and flexing the balance of resources and facilities allocated to each stage of the process. 'Trigger points' will also need to be agreed with each specialty for when whole hospital action may be required: switching operating time between specialties for example, or allocating additional theatre time to a specialty from previously unallocated capacity.

Whilst purchasers will need to be confident that providers are developing their own ability to manage patient flow effectively, there are aspects of patient flow management for which purchasers should take a lead responsibility. These focus in particularly on the 'demand' side, and might include, for example, an enhanced understanding of GP referral patterns and their appropriateness, encouraging dialogue between GPs and hospital consultants on the effectiveness of those referrals, and leading the development of jointly agreed clinical protocols for referrals, GP management of chronic conditions, hospital treatments and discharge procedures.

An enhanced understanding of patient flow at both provider and purchaser level will serve to inform the contract negotiation process. Providers will be able to identify in these discussions, the need for provider action. Purchasers, for their part, will be able increasingly to set purchasing priorities and contract resource levels to reflect their discussions and agreements on referral levels and patterns.

Arising from these initiatives will be the development of contracts or service agreements which explicitly include waiting time targets and improved waiting list management as a means of improving performance. This will help to ensure that purchasers give themselves every opportunity to meet their responsibilities in relation to the targets set in partnership with their main providers. In order to sign up to these,

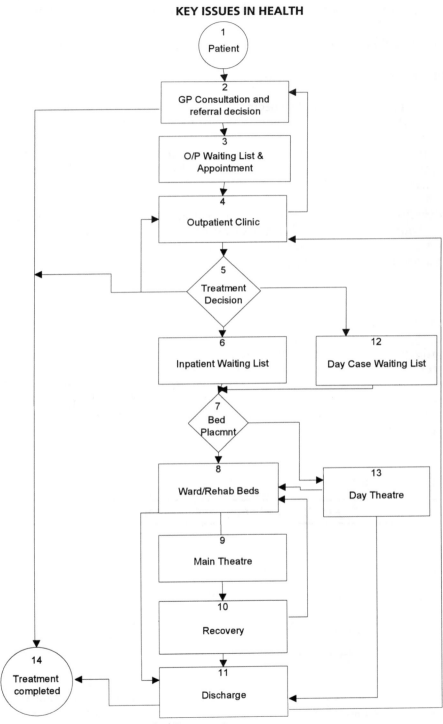

FIG. 4.3 Patient Flow: Surgical Treatment

providers would need to be reassured that such contracts would take explicit account of changes in referral rates. However, the advantage of bringing waiting time into contracts in this way are that:

- waiting time is brought specifically into monitoring arrangements;
- incentives to reduce waiting time can be linked to the contracting process;
- the relationship between referral rates, activity levels and waiting time is made much more explicit than hitherto has been the case.

Finally, the *Good Practice Guide* can be used as a means of allocating future waiting list monies. With the opportunity to assess how each bid demonstrates movement across the continuum towards best practice in the management of waiting time.

Patient Charter

Initiatives in benchmarking in England have concentrated on patient charter issues. Firstly key factors have been identified and then standards of performance have been established. Both the waiting times work and these examples have used 'maturity grids' to help present standards or good practice in a way which is easy for practitioners to use and make self-assessments.

TABLE 4.1 Key Factors by Service Area

Outpatients	Accident and Emergency	Inpatients
Waiting in OPD	Initial assessment	2 year guaranteed admission
Use of services	Privacy and dignity	Named nurse
Complaints	Information to relatives and friends	Discharge
		Cancellation of operations

The following tables illustrate two examples of some of the key factors defined for two standards – the named nurse or midwife and cancellation of operations.

TABLE 4.2   Key factors: Inpatient Services. Named Qualified Nurse, Midwife or Health Visitor

Poor practice	Better practice	Good practice
Informal allocation of Nurse; no monitoring; frequent non-compliance	System exists; little monitoring; non-compliance possible	Named nurse always allocated; audit takes place; no occurrences of non-compliance

Table 4.3   Key factors: Inpatient Services. Cancellation of Operations

Poor practice	Better practice	Good practice
Up to 94% of patients receive operation on first date given; ad hoc system to prioritise the rest; problems occur	95%–98% of patients receive operation on first date; system in place to prioritise the rest; some problems occur	99% or more of patients receive operation on first date; effective system to prioritise the rest; no problems occur

The grids help to establish a common understanding of progress towards meeting patient charter or other standards. The maturity of the organisation is readily apparent and a simple data collection exercise allows comparison with other organisations who have achieved higher degrees of maturity. The system is less daunting than a simple success or failure in meeting required standards and allows provider units to see where they are making progress and where they are stuck or slipping back.

Bed Availability and Management

The Audit Commission claimed in 1992 that if all health districts were to use their acute beds as efficiently as the best 25% of districts then the current level of medical inpatient treatment in England could be provided with 27,000 fewer beds – a drop of almost one-third. In order for this to be achieved they suggested the following procedures:

'With the advent of the purchaser/provider split under the NHS reforms, beds are no longer a strategic resource to be determined centrally. They should be used flexibly at a local level in response to workload' (Audit Commission, 1992a p1).

Admissions: hospital managers to monitor referral rates from each GP and promote communication between consultants and GPs, procedures should be clear and regularly reviewed with all admissions to be vetted by an experienced junior doctor. Patients should also be seen by their consultant within an agreed period;

Placement: to ensure correct placement, a clear record of number and location of empty beds and imminent discharges to be maintained;

Planning: plans to exist for temporary peaks in workload which may cause bed shortages and policies on the transfer of wrongly placed patients;

Length of stay: monitoring of individual consultant's LOS for common conditions;

Co-ordination: of bed management at hospital level, with as much devolution as possible to individual wards and clinical directorates.

These changes are aimed at reducing unnecessary admissions, better placement of patients, shorter LOS and fewer empty beds. However the first step needs to be an overall assessment of bed use within each hospital.

Day Surgery

The use of day surgery is a way to reduce waiting lists and to result in a more efficient use of resources. The Audit Commission concluded in March 1992 that a major expansion of day surgery is possible at no cost to the quality of care and claims that at least 95,000 patients could be treated as day cases rather than inpatients if all hospitals achieved as much as the best 25%. (Audit Commission, 1992c).

However, the Commission also outlined some of the obstacles to an expansion in day surgery:

- the lack of data which can be used to compare and monitor day surgery activity;
- availability of dedicated day surgery facilities;
- inefficient and ineffective use of facilities;
- clinicians' preferences for more traditional methods of treatment;

and describes the way forward as:

- development of an agreed strategy which involves consultants in the decision-making process (eg are resources released by day surgery going to be used to increase the number of patients treated or to cut costs, for example by closing a ward);
- development of an on-going commitment to provide resources for day surgery;
- development of day surgery user groups;
- purchasers to increase day surgery activity and to ensure a quality service by stipulating minimum standards of care;
- development of adequate training for surgeons.

Nursing

Nursing in Acute Hospitals: Main Issues

Ward based nursing in acute hospitals is facing a period of significant change. In recognising this, the Audit Commission and others have focused on the following factors:

Inpatient Population: is increasingly older, frailer and in a less stable condition, requiring skilled nursing;

Supply of nurses: the decline in school leavers over the next few years and rising career expectations will challenge trusts/DHAs to improve recruitment and retention of necessary skills;

Project 2000: heralds a change to nursing education with profound implications for staffing the wards;

Management: changes arising out of the NHS reforms will create bold challenges and opportunities.

Related Issues

1. Delivering Better Patient Care

Patient-Centred Care

Care is increasingly based on the needs of the individual rather than on a number of set routines and including continuity of care and the principle that one nurse is *responsible* for an individual's care from start to finish. Although the introduction of the 'nursing process' in the 1980s should have ensured the growth of patient-centred care, this has not happened everywhere. There is little doubt however, that patients prefer being treated as an individual and not as bodies in a bed or as medical diagnoses and that this type of care can enhance the quality of a patient's stay.

Important aspects of this method of care involve:

- abandonment of unnecessary ward routines;
- high-priority care planning, carried out by a nurse who knows the patient with well designed documentation;
- development of standards and ward-based quality assurance systems;
- development of feedback systems to enable quality assessment;
- development of policies for discharge procedure;
- development of clear objectives and ward philosophy. All practitioners to understand and contribute to achieving goals of organisation.

125

2. Staffing of wards/skill mix of staff

Pressure on resources means it is vital that existing staff are deployed in the most effective way. This issue involves:

- the identification of appropriate skill mixes and staffing levels for each ward;
- the use of structures to evaluate the effects on care delivery processes, on patient opinion and on staff of all significant changes to ward staffing levels, skill mix and shift patterns;
- regular reviews of ward activity, workload, and staffing levels (the development of an effective method to help nurses identify their workload is an important issue as doubt has been cast on the currently most commonly used nursing workload management systems);
- assessment of the effects of Project 2000 on skill mix/staffing levels of wards. In 1988, students formed 29% of the workforce, but accounted for well over half the staff on some acute wards – should there be a 'one for one' replacement of learners?
- assessment of the effects on staffing and skill mix of the introduction of Health Care Support Workers and the phasing out of enrolled nurses;
- use of absence and turnover data to identify potential problems;
- identification of a programme of effective post-registration training;
- the renegotiation of shift patterns to suit ward workload – with introduction of flexible rostering as an alternative to employment of bank and agency nurses.

3. Management

The role of nursing management should be to develop the service to meet patient needs. Issues include:

- clarification of resources;
- devolvement of day-to-day budgets;
- clarification of objectives, in particular of nurse management systems;
- computerisation of patient information;
- liaison between nurse managers and management board;
- development of integrated nursing strategies.

4. Resource Releasing Activities

According to the Audit Commission (1991b):

- a reduction in the overlap between morning and afternoon shifts to one hour could theoretically release resources of £50 million;

- reducing the proportion of nurses time spent on non-nursing duties to 8% would release £40 million;
- containing the costs of managing nurses services to no more than 2% of the nursing pay budget would release £35 million nationally for reinvestment in services and training.

5. Outcomes Measurement
The DoH commissioned a research programme on 'Outcomes measurement and nursing practice' in 1992 and it is expected to report in 1995.

6. Expanding Nurse Roles
The development of nurse practitioners. This is a highly topical issue given the government's wish to reduce junior doctors' hours and its belief that nurses can make a contribution by taking on work previously carried out by medics. However, nurses are likely to resist any move by doctors to delegate to them 'medical dirty work' in favour of expansion to roles where nursing training is a prerequisite and nursing skills are used.

Community Health Services

This has proved a difficult area in which to pursue benchmarking. A Working Group of Community Health Units in Wales undertook an exercise defining key work or business areas, client profiles, influencers or gatekeepers, added value to purchasers and possible performance measures and contract currencies (see Figure 4.4). The group was able to identify services available but had some difficulty in defining the products in terms the commissioners were likely to want to buy. Performance measures and possible contract currencies are particularly difficult to define although some work has been undertaken to define common currencies for health gain across service providers (Welsh Office, 1993). The work is continuing and reflects some major difficulties in fitting community services into the provider framework alongside acute hospitals. A particular danger for community units is that acute hospitals are now well versed in meeting contract requirements from commissioners and may be better placed to respond to the new health gain contracts extending services out into the community in competition with the traditional service provider.

In the meantime most progress in community units has been achieved in developing costing methodologies, for example in the community dentistry services (CDS) (Gwynedd Community Health Unit, 1994). The Gwynedd study sampled 30 CDS providers as to the possible merits of using benchmarking as a means of maximising value to patients. Most were in favour but the most common reservation was that too many

SERVICE DESCRIPTION	USER/CLIENT PROFILE	PURCHASER	INFLUENCERS	CONTRACT CURRENCY
CHILD HEALTH SERVICES:				
Child Health Services Consultant-led Child Health Service for pre-school children. Safety-net clinics provided to complement and supplement services provided by family doctor. Will include specialist medical, nursing and therapeutic services to children with special needs.	Pre-school children (0–4 years); expectant and nursing mothers	DHA	Family doctors; health visitors; primary health care teams; district nursing service; social services; education dept.; community midwives; other professionals	
School Age Children Comprehensive school health service for all children in schools maintained by the Local Education Authority, including specialist medical, nursing and therapeutic services for children identified as having special needs following assessment under provisions of 1981 Education Act.	School age children (5–16 years); parents; headmaster	DHA	Headteachers; school nurses; named doctor and nurse allocated to school; Education Authority; Social Services; Adoption Agency; Social workers; community homes	
Dental Service for Children A dental health service for children; including preventative, screening and treatment services.	Pre-school and school children with special needs/in area of social deprivation	DHA	Teachers; healthcare professionals	
Child Protection Child protection service, provided alongside Child Health and School health provision, including Health Visiting, medical and administrative back-up services. Monitoring families and children "at risk" or "potentially at risk" of child abuse and following up actual cases of child abuse.	Pre-school and school children "at risk"; families "at risk"	DHA/Social Services	Health visitors; Social Services Dept.; Police; NSPCC; family doctors	

FIG. 4.4 Community Health Service Descriptions

variables exist which affect the cost of providing the service and hence make useful comparisons difficult. The next stage will therefore merge the costing with process mapping to focus on cost drivers which are a priority for improvement.

Community Nursing: Main Issues

The renewed focus on primary care reinforced by the *Health of the Nation*, (DOH, 1992) and the growing policy emphasis on care in community settings has raised the profile of community nursing.

Recent Developments

- Extension of GP fundholding scheme to cover district nursing and health visiting has introduced additional purchasers of community nursing.
- The need for purchasers to continue a focus on primary health-care was made clear by NHSMEs statement of priorities for 1993–94.

These developments have brought into focus questions about the need for, and deployment of, community nursing.

Issues

A recent study (Baldwin S, 1992) by the social policy unit and the centre for health economics funded by the DoH, outlined the following key issues:

- prioritisation of the community nursing needs of the local population;
- definition of the roles of district and health visiting services;
- development of appropriate measures of service outcomes;

and for:

- Purchasers:
    collaboration with other agencies;
    improvement in understanding of community nursing work;
- Purchasers and Providers jointly:
    local agreement on respective roles;
    harmonisation of approaches to health needs assessment;
    accountability of providers to purchasers;
- Providers
    factors affecting demand and supply;
    service management issues.

Chapter 5
Local Government and Other Public Services

General

Most of this book is based on experience in the health service; the following sections look in more detail at other public service sectors highlighting key issues, monitoring arrangements and existing efforts towards continuous improvement and the opportunity to adopt benchmarking.

This is difficult as, like health, most public sector organisations are subject to constant and radical change, not only in how they are provided but by whom and to what end. The machinery of much of modern local government evolved in earlier periods of relative stability, but from the mid 1980s that stability disappeared and we are now faced with a new round of structural change with the reorganisation of local government. In addition the varying degrees of privatisation, competitive tendering or market testing make it difficult to concentrate on improvements when survival is more likely to be on today's agenda. However it is clear from the interest expressed by former utilities and nationalised industries in benchmarking that the approach will find favour when the dust has settled. A lesson from Xerox is that an early commitment to benchmarking even when very threatened is perhaps the way to survival and sustained success.

Clearly local government already has the benefit of a range of organisations supporting good practice and sharing of experience including CIMA, LGMB etc. A range of comparative statistics are available with CIPFA returns and the newly established Audit Commission Quality

Exchange. From April 1994 local authorities have to publish their performance indicators as part of the Citizen's Charter initiative and comparative tables will be published in 1995.

There has been a strong commitment to securing BS5750 as is evidenced by the number of entries in the 1993 edition of *Quality Initiatives* (ADC, 1993) and a number of organisations like Brent and Grampion have adopted a TQM approach and are claiming or aspiring to be 'best of the best' (Hawkey P, 1994).

However in spite of all this effort Howard Davies, the former Audit Commission controller, is still arguing that many local authorities are 'small minded, grotesquely inefficient ... generally awful' and in need of reform (Davies, 1994).

The answer to this perhaps lies in understanding the stimulus for change in local Government. In some cases it is charismatic leadership, in others the pressure of external competition but as the Audit Commission acknowledge in one of their housing reports 'authorities learn most from each other rather than from published reports and central "guidance"'. 'It is members asking the question, if they can do it in X, why can't we?' that constitutes the most powerful stimulant to local action (Audit Commission, 1986).

Benchmarking is an excellent way of focusing the existing networking. One example is in preparing for compulsory competitive tendering by sharing the load between legal departments (Nicholls and Hann, 1993a). Statutory power exists in s113 of the Local Government Act 1972 for a council to place staff at the disposal of other councils. This section has been amended recently (s113 9I(a)) to authorise councils to also enter into agreements with regional, area, district and special health authorities and NHS trusts. Nicholls and Hann (1993b) argue that the benefits of extending networking to providing actual services allows your council to provide a service 'as comprehensive as the largest local authority within your network' leading to 'improved efficiency and a better quality service'.

What are some of the main issues facing public services?

Local Government Reorganisation

Scotland and Wales are to be reorganised by law into a series of unitary authorities – although change has been delayed until April/May 1995 and debate on the numbers of authorities and their actual boundaries continues.

In England the government is awaiting the recommendations of the Local Goverment Review. It is known that the government is keen to bring England in line with Scotland and Wales as far as the creation of unitary authorities go – although evidence presented to the commission suggests that in many areas public opinion (due to strong local loyalties) supports the status quo.

The review is based on the following issues:

- the changing role of councils due to compulsory competitive tendering (CCT) and devolution for responsibility of services;
- division of functions are difficult to justify, eg it makes more sense for housing, social services and planning functions to be together than apart;
- confusion over who does what in local government, eg significant numbers of council members serve on both county and district councils.

Compulsory Competitive Tendering (CCT)

The government is in the process of introducing CCT for both white collar and blue collar services. While blue collar CCT is well underway the original plan for white collar CCT was that it should be in place by 11 October 1996 with tenders prepared for October 1995. It has now been deferred until after the completion of the Local Government Review – with contracts to be in place 18 months after the creation of the first unitary authorities. As an issue it still continues to exist, as local authorities need to consider the possible implications of the review so as not to be surprised in a few years' time.

Influence of Environmental Factors

'How green is your policy' is becoming an increasing issue for local government. This is particuarly evident concerning traffic policy and its attendant problems – eg efforts to decrease car travel by improving public transport and introducing toll systems for traffic entering towns and cities. Other green issues are the development of cost-effective policies to promote recycling and the controversies surrounding wind farms.

Budgetary Position/Use of Available Resources

The reduction in funding for local government in recent years has been well documented and the issues arising from this are similar to those involved in health:

- the need to make best use of available resources;
- prioritisation of services;
- rationing of services.

Need to Establish a Clear Direction for the Future

Underlying the confusion surrounding reorganisation and other changes in the role of local government in recent years is the central problem that no consensus now exists as to what it is for. The structural changes will place considerable strain on the balance between financial viability and democratic accountability.

Preparations for Reorganisation

With competing submissions still very much in play in order to ensure survival, a great proportion of local government resources (political, professional, technical and consultancy) are directed towards debating the nature, functions, costs and boundaries of the new authorities. A major issue exists in the volume of work that will be needed to ensure a smooth transition of functions. This includes areas such as:

- will authorities cooperate to prepare for new unitary councils – or will DoE and the Welsh Office have to impose joint preparatory structures?
- will authorities losing a particular area look to withhold investment or asset-strip within that area? Will disbanding authorities have to be prevented from unreasonably spending up their balances rather than passing them to successor authorities?

The change is inevitable but joint working with other councils on implementation issues has been slow in beginning and local people's expectations of enjoying the benefits of a unitary structure without suffering the disadvantages of service disruption or increased costs may be frustrated. This requires unitary authorities to ensure they can maintain high-quality services while taking steps to ensure service delivery is integrated and made cost-effective. This is a strong parallel to the situation in health where authorities are seeking to move to commissioning health gain but are having to maintain the purchasing of existing services and now, in Wales at least, have also been instructed to dramatically reduce the number of health authorities and FHSAs (see Figure 4.1).

TUPE: Transfer of Undertakings (Protection of Employment) Regulations 1981, Implementing the 1977 European Acquired Right Directive

Under TUPE, the UK rules say that if a commercial undertaking is transferred to a new employer he or she must safeguard pay and conditions of existing staff including union recognition or face claims for unfair dismissal. When drawing up the rules, the UK government interpreted the EC directive as applying only to the private sector, but a series of decisions in the European Court of Justice has meant that contracts won by private companies from public bodies have been drawn into the net.

Contractors are obviously alarmed by this – having to comply with these regulations would remove their main advantage over in-house bids: the ability to reduce costs. The government is also somewhat irked by this turn of events and is campaigning within the EU to have the directive changed. In the meantime they have issued a set of guidelines (September 1993 and updated January 1994) intended to clarify the issue and strike a balance between remaining within the law and stopping 'anti-competitive behaviour'. However until (if) the law is changed TUPE is an issue with serious side effects for CCT and it continues to confuse and occupy a large amount of local government time.

Impact on Health

The changes that emerge from the Local Government Review will have a major impact on community care, child protection and mental health as social services departments fragment into smaller units, eg in Gwent reorganisation could mean that there will be five child protection committees instead of one.

A major problem again is the uncertainty which makes forward planning difficult.

The following sections look at some of the key issues facing local government services.

Education

Education has like other services moved to a more business like approach with the introduction of local management in schools (LMS) introduced in the 1988 Education Reform Act. In Wales, since April 1993 all county and voluntary aided schools have been funded according to a formula set out in each LEAs statutory scheme for local management of schools. By April 1994 all secondary schools should have delegated budgets (primary by 1995). The Act also removed LEA responsibility for higher education, introduced city technology colleges which are run independently of LEAs and removed the power of LEAs to set schools admissions limits.

Grant maintained (GM) schools in Wales receive their funding directly from the Welsh Office. In England from April 1994 the Funding Agency for Schools took over financial control of grant maintained schools. In any authority where 10% of schools are opted out grant maintained the agency takes shared control and if 75% of schools are opted out the agency takes control of all schools in that area.

The agency has three duties:

- calculation and payment of recurrent, special purpose and capital grants and loans to GM schools;
- financial monitoring of GM schools including value for money studies;
- ensuring the provision of sufficient school places.

All schools should have a corporate school development plan setting out priorities for action. The Schools Management Task Force (SMTF) in the Welsh Office have supported these developments with a number of guides including *Planning for School Development* (SMTF, Jan 1990) and *Development Planning: A Practical Guide* (SMTF, June 1991).

In July 1992 the Secretary for State unveiled his White Paper *Choice and Diversity* promising a framework for schools and maintaining the commitment to testing and the national curriculum. The testing debate continues but the 1992 Education (Schools) Act caused a dramatic reform of the system of schools inspection.

Under the Act, Her Majesty's Chief Inspector of Schools (HMCI) has the broad statutory duty to keep the Secretary of State informed about standards of achievement, quality of education, efficiency of management and the development of values in schools. They also oversee the new system of school inspections.

The Act places on HMCI the duty to ensure that each secondary school (from September 1993) and each primary or special school (from September 1994) is inspected once every five years by a team of independent inspectors. The new inspectors are assessed and accredited.

The inspections cover:

- the efficiency with which the schools financial resources are managed;
- the spiritual, moral, social and cultural development of the schools pupils.

It is intended that the school 'will see the report as a useful device for encouraging the continuation of school improvement' (Clwyd County Council, 1993).

The 'Main Findings' of the report should be consistent with its general tenor, and should contain the essence of the inspection team's overall judgement of the quality, standards, efficiency and ethos of the school. The report concludes with 'Key issues for action' which should set out clearly the most important matters to be addressed. The guidance observes that these issues 'should relate directly to weaknesses observed in the course of inspection; they should not reflect particular predilections of those carrying out the inspection, for example, for certain styles of management, teaching methods or forms of organisational systems.'

(*Handbook for the Inspection of Schools*, OHMCI, 1992, p14, revised 1993).

On receipt of the written report, the governors of the school have 40 working days in which to produce an action plan which outlines the steps which are to be taken to address any problems identified. The final report is a public document and is made available to libraries and the media.

The action plan should set out:

* the action planned;
* the person responsible for taking action;
* a timetable for action;
* criteria for judging the success of the action in meeting its objectives.

Some of the issues identified in early reports are simply pointing out deficiencies in balance of time given to aspects of the national curriculum or local agreed syllabus or to the need to complete internal management arrangements. Other actions are more difficult to put right for example 'the need to pursue strategies to improve rates of attendance, particularly for pupils whose learning and achievements are adversely affected by frequent absence from school.' (Inspection under Section 9 of the Education (Schools) Act 1992, ISBN 0/7504/05320). In such areas the opportunity to learn from others can no doubt save much effort and frustration.

Wiltshire County has established an Education Support and Training (WEST) Unit which seeks to facilitate networking of good practice across the County and to 'broker' the skills, expertise and understanding of successful practitioners between institutions.

In April 1994 the Office for Standards in England and the Office of HM Chief Inspector of Schools in Wales published details of case studies offering practical guidance on how schools can improve. (OFSTED, 1994).

The report suggests that planning for improvement has not been a strength of British Schools but some do demonstrate genuine improvement through careful rational planning and the commitment of teachers, heads, pupils and governors.

First we must be very clear about the existing state of things. Next we need a clear vision of what it should look like when the improvement we want has been achieved but we do not have to do this alone.

'It is important to have cross fertilisation and share experience.' (McGill, 1994 p4, 15.4.94).

Further Education

The White Paper *Education and Training for the 21st century* set out the agenda for change in further education. The Paper emphasised that the primary responsibility for quality should rest with colleges as they became incorporated and free of their LEAs. The Further and Higher Education Act 1992 removed colleges of FE and sixth form colleges from LEA control and made them self-governing with their funding arrangements transferred from 1.4.1993 to the Further Education Council (FEFC) and the Further Education Council for Wales (FEFCW). The Act also passed the responsibility for securing quality assessment in institutions within the new further education sector to the new funding councils.

In November 1992 the first part of a two-stage process was introduced by the Further Education Funding Council (FEFC) for the preparation of collegiate strategic plans. The second stage which added accommodation to the existing topics of enrolments, quality and staff planning and development was confirmed in January 1994 (FEFC Circular 94/01). The circular asks colleges to describe their arrangements for quality assurance taking account of the criteria in the inspection framework set out in Circular 93/28. OHMCI (Office of HMI of Schools in Wales) may carry out quality assessments in the new FE sector at the request of the FEFCW.

The 1993 report of the FEFC *Assessing Achievement* pointed out that 'good practice is sometimes achieved in poor accommodation with poor resources. By contrast poor teaching and learning sometimes occur in excellent accommodation supported by good resources'.

Key Issues

- Diversity of sector
- Pressure to expand
- Need to produce annual efficiency savings
- To deliver more relevant curriculum
- To compete and collaborate
- To be accountable to the funding councils
- Shared funding: FEFC, TECs, European Social Fund, external income generation

---

Higher Education

Key Issues

Drive for University Status
There is increased competitive pressure on polytechnics and colleges of HE to achieve a status they may not all wish for. Some commentators argue this may lead to a decline in overall educational standards.

Increased Numbers of Students
Demand was encouraged to outstrip 'supply' in 1993/94. In 1994 capping on expansion is to begin. Colleges have been encouraged to increase numbers of places over the past five years, without a corresponding 'real' increase in funding. The pressure in the system for rationing and improved utilisation of resources is about to move centre stage.

Funding Settlements 1994/95
Funding allocations for 1994/95 appear as an attempt at consolidation, with settlements from 1%–6.8%, though controls on how money is spent will be stronger with the establishment of a Higher Education Funding Council for England Audit Committee.

Decisive factors in this year's funding round have been: outcomes of most recent research and allocations for part-time work. Allocations still assume growth of 5.8% taking enrolment to 1.14 million; 748,000 full-time and 366,000 part-time. Institutions who take in greater than contracted numbers will have equivalent sums withheld. Those who take in less numbers than contracted will face a holdback of funds in 1995/96. Also it is becoming clearer that over the next three years, colleges will receive a 10% cash cut per student.

The conclusions that can be drawn suggest that in effect the HEFCE are acting as a customer, providing funding for teaching specified numbers and research in specified areas – so colleges will need to secure business from more than one customer. The parallels with purchasing of hospital treatments suggests higher education institutions may have something to learn from hospitals who have developed successful provider strategies.

Research Funding
Of those institutions that have been funded for research (ie the old universities) by the English Higher Education Funding Council, no institution averaged less than grade 3 (ie research of national or international excellence). However, 7 of these institutions were only receiving 2%

additional funding, and 13 only 3.5% – increases that are modest compared with the rate of inflation.

Research assessment is being troubled by 'spurious' outcome measures and a contestable behavioural model; that quality will result from punishment of bad research. Less thought is being given as to what constiutes good research, or good teaching processes, or what contribution academe can make to education, society and economy.

At the moment research is also being placed in a Catch 22 situation – departments need a constant flow of 'quality' publications but find their research time being eaten away by increasing numbers of students, increasing administration and the possibility of longer terms.

Quality

The Higher Education Quality Council was set up to look at the quality assurance systems in universities. In 1994 it was criticised by its self-commissioned report for ineffective public communication. Whilst praising the council's effectiveness in raising awareness and promoting quality control systems within universities it was failing to explain the relevance of its role or the reason for the emphasis on quality.

John Stoddart, Vice Chancellor, Sheffield Hallam University, Chair of The Higher Education Quality Council described his view. 'What the academic community should have are systems which force them to look outside, to comparisons with other countries, and to seek educational links with those other countries. I see it as a looking out, rather than a looking in.' (in Jenkins, 1994 p15).

Social Services

The NHS and Community Care Act 1990 required local social services authorities to move from being the suppliers of a range of services to taking on the lead agency role. They are now required to assess the needs of individuals and arrange from the provision of appropriate individual services to them.

The Audit Commission report *The Community revolution: personal social services and community care* (1992e) identified three major issues:

- refocusing on users rather than services;
- challenge of identification of needs and resources and priority setting budget allocation;
- closer policy development and working together, eg hospital discharge.

The DoH policy guidance encouraged the development of 'seamless care' by requiring that the 'boundaries between primary health-care, secondary health-care and social care do not form barriers seen from the perspective of the service user' (DoH, 1990).

The Commission commenting on working together and 'seamless services' recommended services should:

- practice 'involvement' with the NHS rather than simply consultation;
- agree distinctions and responsibilities between health and social care;
- develop closer liaison with housing agencies with joint reviews of dependencies and agreements on support in sheltered housing;
- involve independent organisations in the planning process;
- agree and implement arrangements for discharging patients from acute hospitals and for providing them with care in the community.

Each local social services authority is now required to produce a Community Care Plan (CCP). Authorities need to define and identify need within the whole community. The DoH provided a 'key indicator' package to support this process. Priorities should be established and 'target groups' identified. Budgets will then be allocated to Care Managers who will purchase services from within and outside the authority. Separate budgets will be used for those who do not need a personal care manager.

Key issues for departments are the amount of budget and discretion they devolve to care managers, the timing of this and the level of financial management support they provide.

Other key issues for social services include:

Non-accidental Injury
The 1989 Children Act places a responsibility on all local authority departments not just social services to work together. Area Child Protection Committees for example are intended to reduce the risks of lack of coordination contributing to children being at risk but the recent NCB Report *Shape up or shake up (1994)* by Jones, and Bilton, suggest that more effective working is required.

Housing and Homelessness
The Children's Act 1989 Part III and the Housing Act 1985 Part III indicate a clear duty for agencies to provide or secure the provision or give assistance in relation to the securing of accommodation. But the legal opportunities for gaps between agencies are still there (as Andrew Arden QC and Christopher Baker have demonstrated, 1993).

Arrangements for Discharge from Hospital
Gwent Social Services and Nevill Hall Hospital are cooperating in a benchmarking project reviewing current discharge arrangements in search of best practice (NHSBRC, 1994c).

Children's Homes

Key issues identified by Norman Warner, Chair of the 1992 Government Inquiry on selection, development and management of children's homes staff (1994) following the Frank Beck case include:

- recruitment
- unsafe selection
- poor supervision of staff
- inadequate training to cope with difficult children
- low morale
- shortage of specialist educational services and psychiatric support.

(quoted in *The Guardian* 30.3.94).

The inquiry also revealed that the worst management practices tended to be among the smaller authorities.

Reorganisation of Local Government

This will have the effect of creating many more departments at the same time as health authorities and FHSAs are being obliged to merge into much larger organisations. In November 1993 an increase of social service departments in England from 108 to 150–175 and a decrease from 145 HAs and 90 FHSAs to 80–90 new integrated health authorities was envisaged.

Key Issues again identified by Norman Warner (*LGC*, 26.11.93) will be:

- Maintenance of specialist services such as adoption, residential child care, child protection specialists and mental health.
- Senior management, planning and policy sections need to be able to attract high calibre staff.
- Critical mass of support services, eg personnel and finance services.
- Resourcing information technology.
- Relationships with health. In Wales the county councils and health authorities are at present coterminous. Fragmentation and contrasting scales may adversely affect the relationships.

Planning for Rights of Way

Planning has gone through many changes and fortunes, with recent revival in interest for strategic and local planning. However, activity over the last few years has concentrated on development control, design guidance in urban and rural areas and making better use of natural and man made amenities.

Making better use of the existing path network has become a prominent issue in recent years following the Countryside Commission's 1987 policy statement *Policies for enjoying the Countryside*, which singled out the rights of way (RoW) network as the 'most important means by which the public can enjoy the countryside' and set as its target 'the entire rights of way network to be legally defined, properly maintained and well publicised by the turn of the century'. The Commission followed this up in 1989 with *Paths, Routes and Trails: policies and priorities* which prompted the still continuing battle with access groups over the validity of seeking to define *a* network as opposed to affirming and developing *the* network.

In 1987 the Countryside Commission in England and in Wales set highway authorities the target of having all 140,000 miles of rights of way open and enjoyable for the public to use, and properly recorded on definitive maps by the end of the century.

The target was set in Wales in 1987 when what was described as 'a benchmark survey' was conducted to establish ROW involvement at that time. Another study undertaken in 1992 sought to establish progress. Total expenditure on maintaining and administering rights of way in Wales in 1992 was nearly £3.5m, an increase of 67% since 1987.

TABLE 5.1

County	Total ROW Length Kms	Expenditure in £s	Expnd per head £s	Expnd per ROW km £s	Expnd per Sq Km £s
ENGLAND	183448	22326500	0.61	143.15	198.03
South Glamorgan	724	133700	0.33	184.67	321.16
Clwyd	4184	422800	1.03	101.05	174.07
Dyfed	9616	553700	1.57	57.58	95.92
Gwynedd	6390	1074800	4.47	168.20	277.93
West Glamorgan	1435	284400	0.78	198.19	348.00
Mid Glamorgan	2020	334300	0.62	165.49	327.21
Powys	10000	419700	3.59	41.97	82.66
Gwent	4080	229700	0.51	56.30	167.18
WALES	38449	3453100	1.20	89.80	166.20

Source: *Local Authorities expenditure and activity on rights of Way*, Survey Research Associates for the Countryside Council for Wales. Vols 1 & 2, Sept 1992.

CCP 395, *Local Authorities expenditure on rights of Way*, Survey Research Associates for the Countryside Commission, 1993.

By 1992 only six authorities (of 27) confirmed they had adopted the target. Clwyd and Gwynedd expected to meet the target by 2010, Mid Glamorgan by 1998. Five County Councils who failed to adopt the target blamed a lack of manpower or financial resources or felt the target was impractical, onerous or unreasonable. The experience in England was similar. The Wales report usefully published a chart of planning and practical implementation of ROW tasks by county, national park authority and district. This provided the opportunity for those authorities struggling to adopt or meet the target to consider the efforts of their neighbours.

Recently the Countryside Council for Wales have confirmed their commitment to see the entire network opened by 2000 with an interim target of a network opened by 1995 (CAMRE, 1994).

The Ramblers' Association (RA) is an interesting example of a voluntary organisation which is attempting to marry its campaigning role and its support of its members enjoyment with a new role in advising and 'carrying out' statutory duties of footpath recording and clearance.

To support good practice, the Association produces guidance for RA footpath workers which includes good practice or 'checklists' on:

- general principles;
- the consultation process;
- path orders;
- publication of the notice accompanying the order;
- the public inquiry etc.

Footpath Worker, a quarterly bulletin, contains reports of decision letters on public path orders, court cases and other matters of interest to those concerned with maintaining and accessing paths. *Rights of Way: A guide to law and practice* is recognised as the definitive work on the subject and at its annual AGM, there is always a lively session on bright ideas.

At the 1994 AGM, it was clear that there were considerable disparities in local group footpaths officers' ability to cope with the demands of footpath diversions, paths affected by planning proposals as well as maintain the democracy of consulting the wider membership of the local groups. Some groups had achieved this however by entering the formal local process earlier. In several areas the local RA group had invited landowners to discuss possible diversions before making a formal application to the local authority. This was in addition to negotiating the right to be consulted on all path diversions.

The Local Environment Charter *Your Council and the environment* (DoE, 1993) sets out the standards local people can expect from local authorities including maintaining and signposting rights of way, clearing obstructions and keeping the definitive map of rights of way up to date.

Specific good practice quoted includes:

- responding to complaints about rights of way within 14 days;
- removing obstructions within three months of an inspection.

The Health Promotion Authority for Wales and the Countryside Council for Wales have recognised the value of countryside recreation towards maintaining good health and recently promoted with local councils and voluntary organisations the 'Lonc a Chlonc' (Walk and Talk) campaign which encourages those at risk of poor health to combine walking, talking and enjoying the countryside (CCW, 1993).

Housing

The role of housing in local government has moved from being primarily a provider of social housing to an enabler of meeting housing need.

Local authorities retain primary responsibility for the maintenance of council housing but they no longer have full control over their resources. Until 1989–90 they could use capital receipts for maintenance purposes but by 1992 this was set at a maximum of 25% and many authorities had responded by transferring their stock to housing associations who are set to become the main providers of social housing.

Local authorities have a statutory duty to review the housing needs of their local area. The White Paper: *The Governments proposals* (9.87) and the *Housing Investment Programmes* guidance notes (1990, 1991) defined the new strategic role for local authorities as:

- reviewing and improving the quality of local housing strategies;
- identifying housing needs and demands;
- encouraging innovative methods of provision by others.

The strategies must deal with three areas:

- rehousing;
- maintaining the local authority stock;
- supporting improvements to the condition of housing in the private sector.

In England annual allocations are made within the Housing Investment Programme (HIP) against which the housing authorities make bids. In

1993 authorities were also required to produce a housing strategy document and to make a presentation to an invited audience of tenants, representatives from the building and construction industries, members of the Housing Corporation and others with an interest in housing. The strategies are expected to be developed in consultation with the Housing Corporation, housing associations, the private housing sector and tenants' groups.

In Wales following the publication of *Housing in Wales, An agenda for Action* in 1991 discretionary allocations have been linked to the local authorities housing strategy and operational plans (cf HIP). The Welsh Office holds annual review meetings with each local authority to discuss the plans in detail.

Key Issues

- Mixed economy: public, local authorities, housing corporation, housing associations, private
- Joint responsibilities for strategy with social services: Children's Act S20 (1989) duty on social services authorities to provide accommodation for children over 16 whose welfare would otherwise be prejudiced
- Identification of local need
- Demand control
- Backlog maintenance
- Falling receipts
- Good quality and usable surveys of housing stock
- Matching need to stock
- Incentives to buy, transfer or enter private sector
- Letting procedure
- Waiting times, voids

Letting Procedure

A model letting procedure was highlighted in *Managing the Crisis in Council Housing* (Audit Commission, 1986). This shows how an authority can make best use of its housing stock by achieving rapid relets by effective coordination of function and target setting (see Figure 5.1).

LOCAL GOVERNMENT

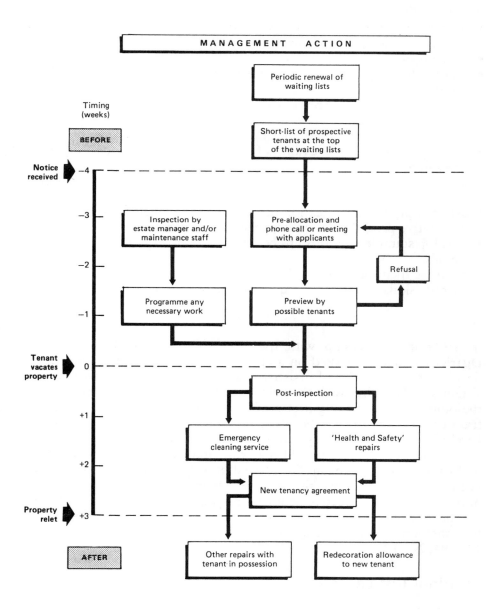

FIG. 5.1 Letting Procedure (Audit Commission, 1992f)

The Audit Commission (1992f) recommends as good practice that housing authorities:

- undertake a systematic and fundamental reappraisal of their housing role and those of other housing agencies;
- set comprehensive objectives;
- identify housing needs in all tenures and establish means of prioritising them;
- undertake a comprehensive assessment of internally generated and external resources;
- make the best use of their housing stocks;
- identify a comprehensive range of alternative options for meeting priority needs;
- establish a methodology for evaluating the relative merits of options and hence comparing them;
- set up a programme creation process which highlights the impact of alternative programmes on key measures of performance;
- develop suitable relationships between departments and with extenal bodies;
- measure their outcomes and re-evaluate strategies;
- identify skills and training requirements for an effective strategic role.

Quality Initiatives

In 1990 in partnership with the Welsh Office, Wrexham Maelor District Council embarked on a customer care programme. The team decided that BS5750 with its structured approach would ensure consistent standards but with the help of external consultants agreed that the objective of achieving best practice within all housing department transactions and locations was the objective rather than simply BS5750 certification. A key activity was the formulation and agreeing of service level agreements (SLAs) with other directorates and these SLAs were included in the 50 internal audits. Any areas or activities not operating to best practice standards were issued with non-conformity reports and corrective action was agreed and dated. By 1994 the certification had been achieved and the department is now keen 'to face the continuing challenge of maintaining quality standards'. (MJ, 11.3.94, No 10).

Criminal Justice

Probation

The Home Office report *Three year plan for the Probation Service 1993–1996*, set out the service's core responsibilities and goals. The plan superseded the 1984 Statement of National Objectives and

Priorities, drawing together the strands of policy affecting the probation service and the expected broad direction. The plan suggested it should 'act as a benchmark against which the government will judge progress in the achievement of its priorities'. Services are expected to implement the Criminal Justice Act 1991 and to implement the new national standards prepared in respect of pre-sentence reports (PSRs), probation orders, supervision orders, community service orders, combination orders, the management of hostels and supervision before and after release from custody. Services were required to set local targets in respect of standards. These were expected to cover quantifiable elements (eg timeliness of PSRs), outcomes (eg % of proposals accepted) and qualitative measures.

Central work continues in developing a 'quality instrument' and in developing a range of high level performance indicators.

The government strategies for the probation service for 1994–97 include:

- the effective operation of the criminal justice act 1991 as amended;
- implementation of and full adherence to national standards;
- strengthened capacity to deal with serious offenders, many of whom have special needs;
- strengthened management, financial and information systems and increased collaboration;
- further development of inter-agency working and partnership;
- management of the additional demand from the Children's Act 1989 – providing a service to the courts which maintains the quality of reports but reduces backlogs;
- the application of the citizen charter principles across the range of probation service work.

The aims of local services vary in detail but follow the common themes set out by the Home Office. They usually include the following:

- to contribute to the reduction in crime in the community;
- to provide the courts with a range of effective community sentences;
- to reduce re-offending by those under supervision;
- to promote the best interests of children in family proceedings.

Within these overall aims, quality aims are also articulated for example the Leicestershire Probation Service aims 'to be an organisation which pursues continual improvement in quality of services'.

The expectation is that each probation service would set their own objectives within each goal area. HM Inspectorate of Probation then assesses the progress of each service against the three-year plan as part of their programme of efficiency and effectiveness inspections.

Cheshire Probation for example have set out their local key objectives as illustrated in Figure 5.2.

Key objective: Through the provision of pre-sentence reports (PSR) to secure the most effective use of community sentence.		
Strategy	Units Responsible	Performance Indicators
To deliver PSRs to the quality required in national standards and effectively gatekeep and monitor them	Field Teams Crown Court Teams	– % coverage PSRs in cases with guilty pleas and findings of guilt – % congruance between sentence passed, seriousness and restrictions of liberty scales assessed by PSR author – % completion standard monitoring form

Cheshire Probation Service: Service Objectives for 1993/4, Cheshire Probation Service, 3.1993

FIG. 5.2

The service has gone through a shift in focus in recent years and the social work origins which tended to treat those on probation as 'clients' has given way under the pressures of new central policy and legislation to a service which recognises 'users' of services which includes defendants, offenders and family court work clients and 'interested bodies' including the Home Office, the courts, county and district councils and the Prison Service Agency. There are of course particularly close links with social services, housing departments and housing agencies and the health service and the Prison Health Authority.

Key Issues

- Cash limited budgets
- Market testing and competitive tendering
- Local government reorganisation
- Increased collaboration between probation areas
- Introduction of probation boards (The Probation Board: the new role and shape of probation committees, HO, 3, 92 and CPO letter 43/92)

- Changes to probation staff codes and conditions
- Expected patterns of employment, training and qualifications for probation staff
- Expected legislative changes to Criminal Justice Acts 1991 and 1993
- Uncertainties about impact on policies, practice and resource needs

Police

All forces are subject to inspection from the HMI of Constabulary. In addition the Audit Commission has carried out a number of reviews.

Several forces have recently undergone reorganisation and rationalisation. The Cumbria service has established a performance review department to include the Force Inspectorate, Quality Assurance and Management Information Unit. The Inspectorate is responsible for undertaking full and thematic inspections into systems and procedures to ensure they are efficient and to promote good practice. A quality assurance help desk provides assistance and guidance to the force on quality assurance matters.

Several of the forces in the UK have established links with forces overseas. Essex for example has an exchange programme with New South Wales Police who have embraced a benchmarking approach.

The approach of the NSW police is threefold:

- to emulate the best available in the world;
- to constantly seek improved performance;
- to measure it.

The NSW police service has a history of searching for improvements worldwide and implementing them. Copying from other police agencies who are doing well is very common. For example a study of procedures for 'physical evidence' in 1990 involved a comprehensive review of policing agencies in Victoria, South Australia, Queensland, and UK (Metropolitan) and Canada (RCMP, Toronto and Vancouver). NSW police claim there has subsequently been a marked improvement in communications and in the range, quality and delivery of physical evidence services.

In addition to access to worldwide research and training networks and funded overseas study tours, there is an exchange programme with the

Royal Canadian Mounted Police and Essex Police. However the service has recognised the limitations of restricting search for best practice to a traditional comfort zone of other Australian states, Canada, UK and the USA and are now reviewing their policy and area of search.

One result of the approach in NSW has been to shift away from specialist services for special needs, eg 'for child abuse, domestic violence, juveniles, street kids, gays and lesbians, aboriginal people or other ethnic or special interest groups towards special programmes which involved all parts of the service'. (Bell, 1993).

Key Issues

- Financial constraints
- Acceptable Income Generation
- Improved management of services
- Integration of emergency services
- Public Relations and Image
- Morale and Career Progression
- Privatisation and Civilianisation of services

Chapter 6
Benchmarking Case Studies

Benchmarking is being applied in the health service in many areas including:

Operating theatre management & utilisation
Day case surgery
Three-session theatres
Head injuries
Sickness and absenteeism
Hospital pharmacy distribution
Pharmacy dispensing errors
Ward to pharmacy communications
Patient flow management
Communications in A&E departments
Bed management
Patient discharge from hospital
Hospital at home.

Two projects in Wales which are well developed are operating theatre management & utilisation and best practice in drug distribution (see NHSBRC, 1993).

Project Design: Theatre Management and Utilisation

The hospital is a 680 bed NHS trust general hospital. The hospital has a revenue of £53m and employs 1,800 staff. It has the usual mix of general hospital specialties including 90 general surgical beds, 30 urology, 30 ENT, 31 gynaecology and 30 trauma. These specialities are based at the main site, and along with oral and maxillo-facial surgery are serviced by a theatre suite consisting of 6 major and one minor theatre. The throughput is made up of 48,000 consultant episodes, 135,000 outpatient attendances and 36,000 accident and emergency attendances.

The project was established by the hospital as its contribution to the formation of a benchmarking club which also includes six other district general hospitals in Wales and England. The management and utilisation of operating theatres had already been identified by the hospital as a cause of concern and the introduction of the benchmarking approach together with the formation of the club offered an opportunity to pursue this issue. The hospital was also considering increasing its number of theatres to cope with increasing demand. The project has set aims and objectives and follows the standard benchmarking approach described by The NHS Benchmarking Reference Centre, 1992.

Aims and Objectives

The hospital trust wished to demonstrate its leadership as a learning organisation and its commitment to effective use of resources in achieving health gain and commissioner confidence.

This project planned to demonstrate these aims by achieving best practice in theatre utilisation by:

- The comparison of performance levels by specialty by reference to national best in class measures.
- The mapping of process within a target specialty and comparison with best performance within the trust, with colleagues in the benchmarking club and best in class performers elsewhere.
- The development of performance indicators for theatre management.
- The costing of key theatre process areas to agreed standards capable of comparison elsewhere.
- The demonstration of the value of using a benchmarking approach and the sharing of progress with benchmarking colleagues in the DGH benchmarking club.
- The production of a report on best practice for dissemination throughout the NHS.

Plan: Select Subject Area

The hospital thought they were poor at theatre management, but in practice didn't know whether they were poor or not. They chose theatre management as a benchmarking project because theatres have high value and opportunity for improvement.

- Theatres have a major impact on all surgical throughput.
- Theatres represent a vital resource for the hospital.
- Theatres affect contract performance and the quality of treatment.
- Theatres had not been the subject of a previous review.

The other members of the benchmarking club shared the hospital's concerns on how to improve theatre performance. The club agreed to investigate:

- Where is Operating Theatre best practice?
- How is it measured? What are the indicators?
- What are the processes?
- How can we improve?

As they progressed with the study, they realised that it would also be necessary to consider broader issues such as inpatient waiting lists and costing.

Plan: Define Process to Benchmark

This work draws on work already undertaken by other hospitals in Pembrokeshire, Gwynedd and Mid Glamorgan and from the work on patients flow management of orthopaedics waiting lists undertaken at Glan Hafren in Gwent.

There was a recognition from the beginning of the limited value of statistical measures. They cannot be used simply on their own as they tend to highlight symptoms rather than causes of problems. It is essential that the processes behind the statistics are defined. The process-mapping exercise can be slow when learning and is not an easy process. When theatres were chosen as a benchmarking area a series of complex questions arose, however the basic questions for process-mapping are: how do you do it? How far do you go? The hospital tried initially to cover the whole activity of theatres which is too large an area. What they learnt was the need to establish the boundaries of the study and to breakdown the work into bite-size chunks. The hospital felt they needed a detailed understanding of all the elements impacting on theatre utilisation and management, so began to look at all the steps involved. They soon corrected this and began to define component areas, eg patient transfer, patient recovery. In particular they looked at the process involved in calling a patient to the theatre suite (see Figure 6.1). Even the simplest occurrence can have a major effect; for example:

'The porter goes to the ward to collect the patient for theatre. If the patient is not ready there are considerable knock-on effects; the porter has to wait on ward until the patient is ready. Meanwhile back at the theatre a queue of post-operative patients is building up as there is no porter to collect them from recovery. Consequently, as a short-term measure, they may be kept in the anaesthetic room to recover. This then causes delays for other patients on the operative list who may have to be cancelled due to a lack of time. Conceivably, the whole procedure could grind to a halt because of the smallest failure in the system.' (NHSBRC, 1993).

The process-mapping was accomplished by a) observing and b) speaking to theatre staff. They came to realise that you have to consider not only what staff thought happened, but also what actually happened. Another benefit the hospital identified was that benchmarking process-mapping is a useful activity for managers. It gives a better understanding of the department and is an excellent management development technique.

Plan: Identify Potential Benchmarking Partners

At first the hospital had little idea where to find best practice partners. At this stage the failure points were not yet clear but they wanted some external validation of their focus and decided to work initially with the members of their benchmarking club.

Plan: Identify Data Required

The hospital wanted to compare performance with established best practice measures. However, few were available. Those that were related to norms and averages only. There were no best practice measures. They therefore had to develop performance indicators for theatres before they could go any further. They did this using various sources:

- Previous studies – was it possible to pull out indicators?
- NHS Wales high level indicators – some of these were relevant to theatres.
- We asked theatre staff to suggest performance measures themselves.
- Patient Episode Database Wales (WHICH project with support from CHKS).
- Australian indicators.
- Costings.
- The failure points highlighted by the process-mapping.

Some of their first indicators and best practice measures are shown in Figure 6.2.

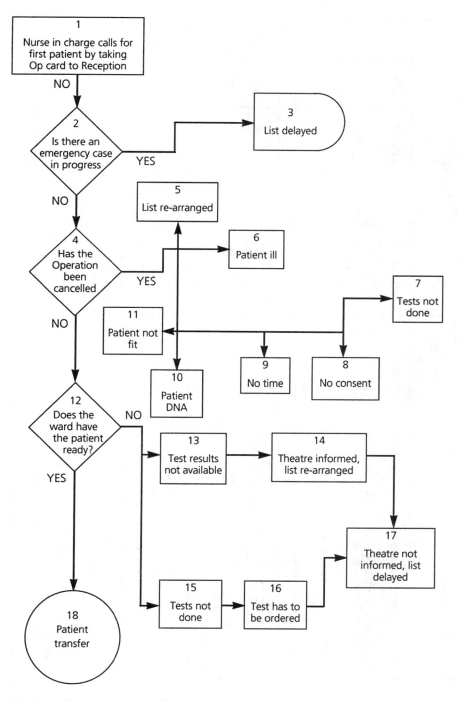

FIG. 6.1   Theatres map — calling patient to the theatre

	INDICATOR (use information for year 1992/93)	Best Practice Guide	Hospital			
			a	b	c	d
1.	**The % of booked sessions per theatre, per week.** *(Total booked sessions for all main & day theatres in a typical week ÷ Total available sessions for all main & day theatres for a week × 100)*	80%	82%	55 (not including trauma) 87.2%	35%	87%
2.	**The average number of cases per theatre per 4 hour session.**					
	All specialties:	4.5	3.3	3.64	5	5
	Gynaecology:		4.79	N/A	5	6
	General Surgery:		2.2	2.75	4	5
	E.N.T.:		4.65	N/A	10	7
3.	**The number of working weeks per theatre per annum.**	50	50	50	49	50
4.	**The ratio of theatres to surgical beds.**	1:45	1:23		1:26	
5.	**The ratio of theatres to surgical cases per annum.**	1:2000	1:1400	1:1294	1:1650	1:1995
6.	**The % utilisation of scheduled theatre time.** **(exclude overruns)** *(Total scheduled time used ÷ Total scheduled theatre time available × 100)*	75–100%	77.5% (approx)	Unable to obtain the information	100%	

FIG. 6.2   Performance indicators for theatres

Analysis: Collect the Data and Select Benchmark Partners

Having identified a set of indicators that were obtainable locally, and which the hospital thought would be useful, they created an indicator questionnaire. There is a limited network for theatres. The club was therefore critical in taking the exercise forward. Within the club theatre utilisation and management was thought to be an important issue. The questionnaire was issued to club members for completion. The club structure it was thought would allow identification of better, if not best practice.

The first results from these questionnaires showed that many of the questions could not be answered. The management information systems and monitoring systems in place do not provide such information. The question the hospitals have started asking is: what is this expensive IT telling us? and is this information useful?

Analysis: Determine the Gap Compared to Benchmark

The information that was collected did confirm that there was considerable variation in performance. The six hospitals demonstrated variation in:

- delays due to missing key staff;
- cancellations;
- interruptions by emergences;
- cost variations.

And whilst each is now seeking to come up to the level of the best in each category, all are also actively seeking best performers.

Analysis: Establish Difference in Process

The hospital now knows where the failure points are and has begun a series of visits to better practice hospitals. One of the staff had the opportunity to visit a hospital in Victoria, Australia as part of a sponsored management training scheme and used this visit to compare the processes in the two theatre suites. He found considerable variation in practice and lessons of value to both organisations. The role of the theatre director in the Australian hospital was clearer.

He spends time in the theatres in a managing role as well as being an anaesthetist. This was demonstrated in the Australian hospital with more effective management of theatre lists to avoid overrunning and in establishing a system of recording utilisation, whereas the Welsh hospital had the advantage of sterilising facilities en suite avoiding transport to an external department. The Australian hospital had very high surgical utilisation of facilities (cutting time) but used them infrequently compared to the Welsh hospital who made less efficient but heavier sessional use of the facilities. There were also noticeable variations in recruitment, training, managing cancellations and overall costs. The Welsh hospital concluded that they were less expensive but had much to learn in organising and using their theatres more effectively (Proctor, 1993).

Analysis: Target Future Performance

This stage requires executive recognition of the scale of the problem and the solution. The timescale, resources and benefits should be clearly expressed as well as the consequences of not doing anything. Implications of the change to other areas of the hospital and up and downstream from the process failure point should be considered.

Action: Communication and Commitment

One of the clear benefits realised in the study is the building of understanding and commitment which comes from asking the 'process owners' what they do, what is wrong and how to improve services if this is clearly linked to action. The hospital undertaking the study has now incorporated benchmarking into all clinical directorates with support and commitment from the board chairman and chief executive.

Action: Adjust Targets and Develop Corrective Improvement Plan

The hospital is committed to be the best but is also subjected to cost constraints. Targets are, of necessity, demanding but the availability of evidence of others' achievement is a strong incentive to believe in the possibility of success.

Action: Implementation

The project is now moving into the implementation phase. The hospital is a resource management site and is therefore familiar with structured project planning using PRINCE type techniques. This requires the setting of achievable targets and milestones within a project plan. Roles and responsibilities are defined as required, resources identified and confirmed as available.

Action: Review Progress and Recalibrate

The project has internal review mechanisms to ensure the plan is on target but the overall project will also be reviewed in terms of cost and disruption against savings and benefits achieved. If the project fails in meeting any of its objectives, these will be reviewed to ensure future projects learn from errors made. If the targets set are found to be over or under ambitious these will be reset in accordance with the experience of the project.

Experience of the project will also be lodged with the Benchmarking Reference Centre to assist in building up the knowledge base of practical benchmarking projects.

Costing

The VFM Unit has been developing cost-tree structures for a number of health services including pathology, radiology, dentistry and pharmacy over the last three years using the commercial programme 'DATA-TREE'. This system is now being used to establish the component costs of one minute of operating theatre time. Two benchmarking club members (Morriston) are now looking at the opportunity costs of scheduling three sessions a day in their operating theatres rather than two. The use of this approach has also allowed them to begin examining the time and cost of process elements to examine which are the true cost drivers and where there are opportunities for re-engineering.

This aspect of the project has a separate set of objectives including the:

- Production of a costing methodology for surgical services encompassing all cost components but concentrating initially on theatre costs.
- The development of a management tool for the evaluation of alternative resource allocation in relation to clarified priorities.

To date the costing of theatre time by specialty has been completed. This has allowed the hospital to make comparisons with other units who have been encouraged to use the same costing system. The most fruitful improvements look to be coming from comparing the costs of three theatre sessions compared to two.

Best Practice

There has been no shortage of advice on good practice (NHSME, 1991), but it is clear that good practice has not been universally adopted. It is emerging from our benchmarking studies that neither comparative data nor ideas of best practice are enough to stimulate change. The benchmarking approach seems to offer the framework to encourage the search for good and best practice by building on existing structures and relationships which already work whilst highlighting the failures and thereby focusing the search for new practices which work elsewhere.

An effective search of available literature (VFM, 1991) is critical in helping to focus the study. For example this project has built on work undertaken in the UK, SW region (bed booking problems), Nottingham (late night surgery problems) and Spain (cancellations, test results delays and non-availability of staff) to ensure we did not miss similar failure points, but we have also used the literature to identify better practice, eg separation of elective from emergency/urgent cases and the importance of planning for the top 20 procedures which account for 70% of work (Frankel, 1991; Ellis, 1991; Corner, 1993).

Results and Action Plan

There has been a pay-back from the exercise and we have already seen positive action being taken. Process-mapping brought out the immediate issues which could be solved easily by managerial action. The 'low hanging fruit' improvements have included resetting and staggering porters' hours to meet the needs of the theatre. Mid-term improvements include the improved relationships between staff, better management of throughput and the further use of the costing system. The real best practice improvements seem likely to come from improvements in use of surgical sessions and scheduling together with the possible introduction of three-session theatres as an alternative to capital investment.

Benchmarking for Best Practice in Hospital Pharmacy

This hospital pharmacy has a reputation for seeking continual improvement in services (Spencer, 1993) and has undertaken a number of studies which contained elements of benchmarking. The pharmacy was therefore well placed to understand the principles of benchmarking and to improve their own approach by adopting the benchmarking framework. The case study highlights therefore how existing approaches can be refocused and absorbed so as to avoid duplicated effort and confusion.

The identification of key issues was recognised as a key stage in the improvement process. In their search for best practice the hospital used a number of methods and criteria.

1. Identifying fail points in the service – an annual satisfaction survey has been carried out among ward managers since 1990. Changes in levels of satisfaction with aspects of the service are readily detected and appropriate actions taken.

2. Gaining knowledge of processes – the department encourages a regular review of procedures and practices in the department and during this process attention may be focused on areas where they feel comparison with other hospitals would be of value.
3. Links with other hospitals – hospital pharmacy in the UK is a relatively small world and news of best practice often gets around quickly offering the opportunity to aim for or improve on the best.
4. Awareness of the literature – the literature on pharmacy practice is relatively small and it is therefore easy to keep up-to-date with published developments elsewhere.
5. Awareness of developments outside the NHS – increasingly the relevance of comparing performance with non-NHS organisations is being recognised.

There is as yet, no directory of best practice in hospital pharmacy, neither is there a body of experience indicating which non-NHS organisations have experience to offer although this is an area that the NHS Benchmarking Reference Centre is seeking to develop. The hospital found that evidence of best practice in hospital pharmacy can be identified through published articles in journals, presentations at conferences and by networking. Best practice in non-NHS organisations can be identified through brainstorming, lateral thinking and developing an interest in the business pages of the national press.

The pharmacy staff recognised that in these relatively early days of benchmarking in the NHS it is necessary that the search for best practice partners must initially be cast wide in order that irrelevant and unsuitable potential partners can be rejected whilst still leaving a number of potential partners in the field. Additionally, they recognised that within the NHS those who publish or publicise are not necessarily the best and that objective measures of success should be sought to corroborate claims. In the outside world also, famous or well known does not always equal best.

Key Issues

Supply of Drugs on Discharge

Ensuring the timely supply of discharge drugs causes significant problems for nursing, pharmacy and medical staff. In addition, patients often feel that they are delayed leaving hospital purely because of the slow turnaround time of discharge prescriptions. Ward managers' satisfaction with the pharmacy's promptness of response to discharge prescriptions has also been consistently lower than desirable. The pharmacy therefore targeted the process for investigation and improvement.

The process, from the moment the patient is told they can go home to the moment the patient receives their drugs, was mapped in detail. Fourteen stages were identified and an exercise was carried out to time each of the stages. This, together with an analysis of the process by pharmacy, nursing and medical staff, identified fail points which often lead to delays.

Simultaneously, a questionnaire survey of 28 teaching hospital pharmacies attempted to identify best practice in other hospitals.

The analysis of the process identified that 50% of the overall time was taken up by the delay between the patient being informed they could go home and the prescription being written. Any improvement in the performance of the stages which nursing and pharmacy staff directly controlled would therefore have had limited effect on overall process time.

The results were presented at one of the weekly grand rounds (at which senior and junior doctors are present) and best practice guidelines aimed at medical staff are being formulated. These will be incorporated into junior medical staff training. In addition the department is reviewing all drug-related policies and procedures and, where appropriate, these will incorporate best practice guidance relating to discharge prescriptions.

Two best practice areas were identified from the questionnaire and other hospital contacts.

Wards are now asked to attach red stickers to those discharge prescriptions which are requested within two hours and a blue sticker to those for which there is no urgency. Work in pharmacy is prioritised on this basis and targets have been set for average turnaround times. Turnaround times are now regularly monitored and compared with targets. The results of subsequent ward managers satisfaction surveys will indicate the success of the changes. In addition, a combined inpatient/discharge prescription sheet is used by some hospitals and was suggested as a way forward by some medical staff. This is now being considered for development within the hospital.

Best Practice in Dispensing

The pharmacy at the hospital dispenses 200,000 items each year. Prior to 1991 the dispensing error rate was unknown. In addition, no published or unpublished data was available which would have enabled comparison with other hospital pharmacies.

Dispensing is a core pharmacy function and it is essential that quality is continuously monitored. The error rate should be considered to be a key control measure. In order to improve the situation the department designed and ran a multi-centre study for six months in 1992. This involved 20 hospitals throughout the United Kingdom collecting a standard data set for all dispensing errors. In addition, the pharmacists provided a written summary of all errors, gave details of the checking systems which they used and provided workload data.

They found that the error rate varied considerably from hospital to hospital and was linked to the checking system used.

The local error rate was 'average' compared to the other pharmacies but the department was not prepared to be complacent and now have a target to improve their error rate to match and ultimately improve on the best of the best. To do this they have begun a phased modification of the dispensing process to utilise best practice from hospitals with low error rates.

In addition, they are continuing to act as a clearing house for dispensing error monitoring on a national basis and currently have 25 hospitals enrolled in the scheme.

Best Practice in Drug Use

In the USA the existence of a Drug Use Evaluation (DUE) programme in a hospital is a key factor in the accreditation decision process by the Joint Commission on Accreditation of Health Care Organisations. In essence, DUE involves setting standards for drug use, measuring performance against the standards, and implementing appropriate corrective action to close any gap. This process can lead to cost savings through the elimination of inappropriate drug use and to an improved quality of care.

With the support of the hospital board the department has established a rolling DUE programme. The results of the first DUE, a study of the use of intravenous Ciprofloxacin, has identified potential savings of £6,000 per year if best practice standards were followed.

Best Practice in Drug Distribution

The above mini case studies, whilst ultimately leading in the direction of best practice, were not originally designed as 'benchmaking' studies. However the department is now formally benchmarking drug storage, stock control and distribution at the hospital against best practice inside and ouside the NHS, in the UK and internationally.

Planning

Drug storage, stock control and distribution was chosen as a subject for benchmarking because it is a core pharmacy function and a high level of performance is essential to success as a department. The subject is of strategic importance to both the pharmacy and the hospital and improvement can lead to increased user satisfaction and minimise stock holdings and wastage without detriment to patient care.

The in-house satisfaction survey indicates that users' perception of service quality could be improved and, although stock turns in the pharmacy and at ward level are among the highest in Wales, the department is keen to determine how they compare in a wider field inside and outside the NHS.

To help focus on the key issues, the overall process was documented in outline. It became clear that technician top up service was a key part of the process to study. This service is the method by which ward and department stocks are checked, maintained and rotated.

Benchmarking Partners

The search for best practice and potential benchmarking partners focused on pharmacy departments in the NHS and outside organisations.

The current partners comprise:

An English NHS Trust.
Chosen because of active development of quality measures.

Selected hospitals in North West Thames RHA.
Chosen because of publication of an annual range of performance indicators relevant to the study.

A pharmaceutical pharmacy and wholesaler.
Chosen because of their links with health and their performance.

A local branch of a high quality and international Company.
Chosen because of its perceived performance.

Data Collection, Process-Mapping and the Future

Using information from two of the benchmarking partners a small project group has been set up in the pharmacy to develop a range of indicators and to collect in-house data.

The process of technician top up has been mapped in detail using a flow charting method (see Figure 6.3). This has been further analysed to help understand the local process in detail and to identify fail points.

These phases are now complete and the department is now visiting partners to compare performance indicators and the processes used. In

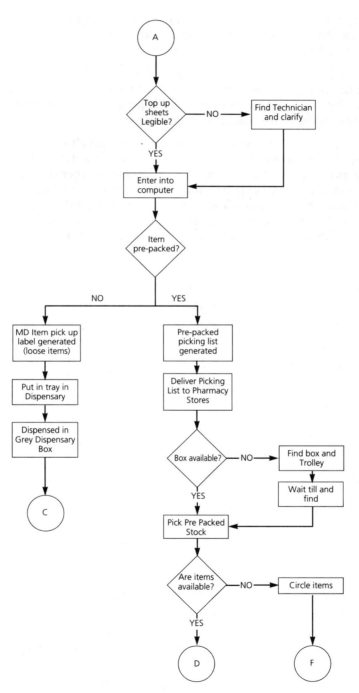

FIG 6.3   Pharmacy process mapping – part of the top up process

addition, those fail points which have been identified which can be eliminated by conventional problem-solving techniques are being addressed in-house.

The hospital pharmacy has set themselves the challenging target of offering the best possible drug distribution service. They aim to do this by achieving superior levels of user satisfaction, a highly cost-effective service and by further improving stock turns.

To achieve this they recognise the need to develop more sensitive measures of performance and plan to achieve this through the benchmarking process. Any performance gap between themselves and best practice organisations will be analysed and process differences determined. Future performance levels will then be targeted and an improvement plan formulated and implemented. Progress will be regularly reviewed. The whole process is planned for completion during 1994.

Bibliography

ADC (1993), *Quality Initiatives: Directory of Local Government Activity*, Local Authority Associations Quality Group.

Andersen Consulting (1993), Cardiff Business School, University of Cambridge, Lean Enterprise Benchmarking Project.

Andersen, A. (1992), *Ambulatory Surgery Best Practices*.

Arden, A. & Baker, C. (1993) quoted in *Local Government Chronicle*, p18/19, 10.12.93.

Association of Anaethetists of GB and Ireland (1989), *Efficiency of Theatre Services*, Sept.

Audit Commission (1986), *Managing the Crisis in Council Housing*, p44, HMSO.

Audit Commission for Local Authorities and the National Health Service in England and Wales (1991a), *How effective is the Audit Commission?*

Audit Commission (1991b), *The Virtue of Patients: Making best use of ward nursing resources*, HMSO.

Audit Commission (1992a), *Lying in Wait: The Use of Medical Beds in Acute Hospitals*, HMSO.

Audit Commission (1992b), *Citizens Charter Indicators: Charting a course*, HMSO.

Audit Commission (1992c), *All in a days work: An Audit of Day Surgery in England and Wales*, HMSO.

Audit Commission (1992d), *Minding the Quality*, A Consultation Document on the role of the Audit Commission in Quality Assurance in Health Care.

Audit Commission (1992e), *The Community revolution: personal social services and community care*, HMSO, London.

Audit Commission (1992f), *Developing Local Authority Housing Strategies*, HMSO, London.

Audit Commission (1993), *What seems to be the Matter: Communication between hospitals and patients*, HMSO.

Baldwin, S., Lightfoot, J. and Wright, K. (1992), *Nursing by numbers: setting staffing levels for district nursing and health visiting services*. Social Policy Unit and Centre for Health Economics, York.

Bell, G. (1993), *Benchmarking in the NSW Police Service*, paper presented at AIC Benchmarking Conference, Sydney 25.8.93.

Bullivant, J. (1991), *The allocation of educational resource opportunities*, p252, PhD thesis, Exeter.

Bullivant, J. and Naylor M. (1992), 'Best of the Best', *Health Service Journal*, 27.8.92, p24–25.

Camp, R. C. (1989), *Benchmarking – the search for industry best practices that lead to superior performance*, SQC Quality Press.

CAMRE (1994), *Draft Strategy for Public Paths*, Countryside Council for Wales (CCW), Feb.

CCP 395 (1993), *Local Authorities expenditures on Rights of Way*, Survey Research Associates for the Countryside Commission.

CCW (1993) Press release on Walk and Talk, Countryside Council for Wales and Health Promotion Authority for Wales (HPAW).

CEPOD (1986), *Confidential Enquiry into peri-operative deaths*, Working Party of the Association of Anaesthetists of GB and Association of Surgeons, also Campling, E. A., Devlin, H. B. and Lunn, J. N. (1990), *The report of the national confidential enquiry into perioperative deaths*, HMSO.

Cliffe, R. (1993), *Using Benchmarking to improve customer service, Quality in Health*, AIC Conference, London, 9.12.93.

Clwyd County Council (1993), *School Inspections, a summary of the arrangements*, Clwyd Advisory Team, CCC.

Codling, S. (1992), *Benchmarking: The management guide to successful implementation*, Industrial Newsletters Ltd.

Concise Oxford Dictionary of Current English (1990), p977, Clarendon Press, Oxford.

Coopers and Lybrand and the Confederation of British Industry's National Manufacturing Council (1993), *Survey of Benchmarking in the UK*, Jan.

BIBLIOGRAPHY

Corner, N. B. (1993), 'Morning emergency operating list: effects of implementation', *Annals of the Royal College of Surgeons of England*, 75, p201–4.

Daily Post (1992), *NHS models itself on world beaters*, 19.11.92.

DoE (1993), *The Local Environment Charter: Your Council and the Environment*, EP 024.

Dalley, G. and Carr-Hill, R. (1991), *Pathways to Quality, a study of quality management initiatives in the NHS*, QMI series No 2, Centre for Health Economics, University of York.

Dalin, P. (1978), *Limits to educational change*, MacMillan, p54.

Davies, H. (1994), Speech to the European Policy Forum, 14.3.94, quoted in *Municipal Journal*, 18–24 March No 11.

Department of Health (1989), *Working for Patients*, Cmnd 555, HMSO.

Department of Health (1990), *Caring for People: Community Care in the Next Decade and Beyond, Policy Guidance*, HMSO, London.

Department of Health (1991), *The Patient's Charter*.

Department of Health (1987), *Promoting better health*, Cmnd 249, HMSO.

Department of Health, Welsh Office, Scottish Office Home and Health Dept and Dept of Health and Social Security, Northern Ireland, (1988, 1991, 1994), *Report on the confidential enquiry into maternal deaths in the UK 1982–84, 1985–87, 1988–90*, HMSO.

Dunshea, R. et al (1994), 'Continuous Improvement in Theatre Utilisation', *Benchmarking Briefing*, Vol 1, No 3, April.

Ellis, E. W. (1991), 'Management importance of common treatments: contribution of top 20 procedures to surgical workload and cost', *British Medical Journal*, 302, (6781) Apr 13, p882–4.

Essex County Council Social Services Advert, *The Guardian*, p18, 30.3.94.

Financial Times Business Toolkit (1994), *Benchmarking to Win*, Video, Longman.

Frankel et al (1991), 'Booked admissions as a replacement for waiting lists in the NHS', *British Medical Journal*, 303, (6812) Nov 16, p1257–8.

Freemantle, N. et al (1993), quoted in 'Talking Shop', *HSJ*, 103 (5357) 17.6.93, p31–33.

Griffiths, Sir R. (1991), *Seven Years of progress – general Management in the NHS*, Audit Commission Management Lecture No 3, June 12.

Gwynedd Community Health Unit (1994), *Determining a charging structure for the Community Dental Service within Gwynedd*.

Hawley, A. and Ferguson, A. (1992), *Marketing in the NHS*, VFM, NHS Wales, September.

Hawkey, P. (1994), 'TQM Awards' in *Municipal Journal* 22.4.94.

Healthcare Forum (1992), Conference: *Benchmarking: the next generation in healthcare quality*, Sept 16–18 1992, Chicago.

Heyward, S. (1991), 'More value for money – learning through doing', *Cost improvement and Income Generation Seminar Report*, Llandridod Wells, 16.9.91, VFM, November.

Humphrey, C. (1986), *The implications of the FMI for the Probation Service*, Dept. of Accounting and Finance, University of Manchester.

Ishikawa, K. (1976), *Guide to Quality Control*, Asian Productivity Organisation, Tokyo.

J&J Hospital Services, Inc (1993), *Profiles in excellence*, J&J, New Brunswick, NJ.

JCAHO (1993), *Accreditation Manual for hospitals*, Joint Commission on Accreditation of Healthcare Organisations.

JCAHO (1991), *Beta I Feedback reports: Obstetetrical care Indicators*, Joint Commision on Accreditation of Healthcare Organisations.

Jenkins, 1994, 'Bearing on standards', *TES Update*, 15.4.94 p15.

Jones, A. and Bilton, K. (1994), *Shape up or shake up*, NCB.

Jones, M. (1994), 'Setting Standards', *Municipal Journal*, 11.3.94, No 10.

Klein, R. and Redmayne, S. (1992), *Patterns and Priorities*, NAHAT.

Kogan, M. (1971), *The Politics of Education*, Penguin, p27.

Local Government Training Board (1985), *Good Management in Local Government*, (gives examples of good practice in local government).

Maxwell, R. J. (1984), 'Quality assessments in health', *British Medical Journal*, 288 pp1470–1474.

McGill, (1994), quoting Mr Clarke, Head of Clayton Middle School, Bradford, *TES* 15.4.94 p4.

MacBurney, R. et al (1993), 'Maximising the benefits of a benchmarking study tour', in *Report of the Benchmarking Convention*, Sydney, 24–25th August 1993, AIC Conferences, Sydney.

National Audit Office (NAO) (1986), *VFM developments in the NHS*, HMSO.

NHS Benchmarking Reference Centre (1992a), *Benchmarking Code of Conduct*.

NHS Benchmarking Reference Centre (1992b), *Benchmarking for Continuous Improvement and Superior Performance in the NHS: (Revised) Notes of Guidance*, September.

NHS Benchmarking Reference Centre (1992c), *Report of the 1st Annual NHS Benchmarking Conference*, November.

BIBLIOGRAPHY

NHS Benchmarking Reference Centre (1992d), *Benchmarking Clubs: A Good Practice Guide.*

NHS Benchmarking Reference Centre (1992e), *Benchmarking Visits: A Good Practice Guide.*

NHS Benchmarking Reference Centre (1993a), *A Good Practice Guide on the use of Consultants.*

NHS Benchmarking Reference Centre (1993b), *Report of the 2nd Annual NHS Benchmarking Conference,* November.

NHS Benchmarking Reference Centre (1994a), *Benchmarking Briefing.*

NHS Benchmarking Reference Centre (1994b), *Process Mapping.*

NHS Benchmarking Reference Centre (1994c), *Discharge from Hospital Project Plan.*

NHS Management Executive (1991), *Problems and Good Practice in Operating Theatres: The Management and Utilisation of Operating Departments,* (Bevan Report).

NHS Wales (1992), *An introduction to the Patient Flow model,* VFM.

NHS Wales (1992), *Waiting Times Good Practice Guides,* VFM.

Nicholls, P. and Hann, R. (1993a), 'Networks that work', *Local Government Chronicle,* 14.5.93.

Nicholls, P. and Hann, R. (1993b), 'Taking the next step towards networks', *Local Government Chronicle,* 5.11.93.

NPRIE eg National Probation Research and Information Exchange (NPRIE) Annual Conference Reports.

Oakland, J. S. (1989), *Total Quality Management,* Heinemann, London.

OFSTED and OHMCI (1994), *Improving Schools,* HMSO.

OHMCI (1992), *Handbook for the inspection of schools* (revised 1993).

Orwell, G. (1937), *The Road to Wigan Pier,* Victor Gollancz 1937.

Parry, J. and Chew, E. (1993), *Benchmarking Clubs — What are they and how do they work,* NHS Benchmarking Conference, Cardiff, 11.11.93, NHSBRC.

PAC, Recommendations of the 10th report (1988–89) of Committee of Public Accounts (PAC) on Quality in clinical care in NHS hospitals.

Pirsig, R. M. (1991), *Lila, An inquiry into Morals,* Bantam Press.

Pokora, D. (1993), article prepared for publication, NHSBRC.

Potter, G. R. (1970), 'Allocation methods in a comprehensive system', *Comprehensive Education,* Summer.

Pozos, A. (1993), 'Benchmarking Customer Satisfaction', in *Report of the Benchmarking Convention, Sydney,* 24–25th August 1993, AIC Conferences, Sydney.

PRINCE (1990), *PRINCE: Structured project management*, NCC Blackwell Ltd.

Proctor, J. (1993), 'Benchmarking Operating Theatres', *GMTS Elective Report*, MCS, WHCSA, Aug.

Ramblers Association, *Footpath Worker*, Quarterly.

Rees, G. and Rees, T. (1980), *Health, Health services and Poverty*, Ch 5, p95.

Riddall, J. and Trevelyan, J. (1992), *Right's of Way: A guide to law and practice*, Commons, Opens Spaces and Footpaths Preservation Society and Ramblers Association, 2nd ed.

Sims, J. (1994), 'Look for best practice', *Healthcare Management*, Feb, p13–16.

SMFT (1991), *Development Planning: A Practical Guide*, Schools Management Task Force.

SMFT (1990), *Planning for School Development*, Schools Management Task Force.

Status Meetings Ltd (1992), *Benchmarking for Competitive Advantage*.

Spencer, M. (1993), *Seeking Best Practice in Pharmacy Services at University Hospital of Wales*, Report of the 2nd Annual NHS Benchmarking Conference, Cardiff, November, VFM.

Survey of Benchmarking in the UK (1993), Coopers and Lybrand and the Confederation of British Industry's National Manufacturing Council, Jan.

Survey Research Associates for the Countryside Council for Wales (1992), *Local Authorities expenditure and activity on rights of Way*, Vols 1 & 2, Sept.

The Benchmarking Centre (1994), 'Common Interest Groups', *Benchmarking News*, Feb.

VFM (1992a), *Benchmarking Briefing Improving managerial performance at Unit level through benchmarking*, March.

VFM (1992b), *Benchmarking for Continuous Improvement and Superior Performance in the NHS, Notes of Guidance*, April.

VFM (1992c), *Welsh Health Information Comparisons for Hospitals (WHICH): A new information service for hospitals*.

VFM (1992d), *Review of Benchmarking in NHS Wales*, September.

VFM (1992e), *High Level Indicators*, Vol. 1 Report: In year monitoring of management performance against a set of High Level Indicators. Vol. 2 Notes of Guidance.

VFM (1992f), *Waiting Times Initiative in Wales: Status Report*.

VFM (1992g), *Benchmarking Look-a-Likes: Accompanying Notes*, August.

VFM Unit (1992h), *Pathology Costing Manual*.

BIBLIOGRAPHY

VFM Unit (1991), *General aspects of an all-Wales review of surgery.*

VFM (1993a), *Patient Flow and Benchmarking: Progress Report.*

VFM (1993b), *Benchmarking for healthy services: progress and plans (1993–95)*, February.

Warner, N. (1993), quoted in *Local Government Chronicle*, 26.11.93.

Warner, N. (1994), quoted in *the Guardian*, 30.3.94.

Watson, G. H. (1993), *Strategic Benchmarking: How to rate your company's performance against the world's best*, John Wiley & Sons.

Welsh Health Information Comparison for Hospitals: A new information service for Welsh hospitals.

Welsh Health Planning Forum (1989), *Strategic Intent and Direction for the NHS in Wales*, Welsh Office/NHS Directorate, Cardiff.

Welsh Office (1988), *The corporate management programme for the health service in Wales 1988–93.*

Welsh Office (1992), *Good Practice in Medical Records.*

Welsh Office (1989a), *Local Strategies for Health: A new approach to strategic planning*, Welsh Health Planning Forum.

Welsh Office/NHS Directorate (1989b), *Agenda for Action*, Cardiff.

Welsh Office (1989c), *Information and Information Technology Strategic Direction.*

Welsh Office (1991), *Housing in Wales, An Agenda for Action.*

Welsh Office/NHS Directorate (1990), *Agenda for Action 2*, Cardiff.

Welsh Office/NHS Directorate (1992), *Caring for the Future*, Cardiff.

Welsh Office (1993), *Advice on Contract Currencies, Contracting for Health Gain Project.*

Welsh Office/NHS Directorate (1994), *Caring for the Future 2*, Cardiff.

Western Mail (1992), *Value for money*, 19.11.92.

Widgery, D. (1979), *Health in Danger, The crisis in the National Health Service*, Macmillan.

World Health Organisation, *Health for All by the Year 2000.*

Wyn Owen, J. (1993), *Report of the 2nd NHS Benchmarking Conference*, VFM, Cardiff.

Useful Contacts

Information Services

NHS Benchmarking Reference Centre
Benchmarking Centre Ltd, Hemel Hempstead
British Library Document Supply Centre, Boston Spa
British Medical Association, London
Council of International Hospitals, Washington
Information Resource Centre, Nuffield
International Benchmarking Clearing House, Texas
Institute of Management, Management Information Centre, Corby
King's Fund Centre, London
Medical Information Centre, British Library, Boston Spa
Office of Population Census and Surveys
Pira International, Surrey
Royal College of General Practitioners
SilverPlatter Information Ltd, London

NHS Benchmarking Reference Centre
Wrexham Technology Park
Croesnewydd Hall
Wrexham LL13 7YP

Tel: 0978 316230
Fax: 0978 316231

Services offered include: gateway services to specialist databases, topic updates, good practice guides, *Benchmarking Briefing* (×5 pa), benchmarking clubs, comparative databases, conferences, training and workshops.

Benchmarking Centre Ltd
c/o Dexion Ltd
Maryland Avenue
Hemel Hempstead
Hertfordshire HP2 7EW
England

Tel: 0442 250040
Fax: 0442 245386

Services offered include: on-line access to UK and USA databases, study tours, conferences, training and workshops, common interest groups.

British Library
Document Supply Centre
Boston Spa
Wetherby
West Yorkshire LS23 7BQ

Tel: 0937 54600 (switchboard)
   0937 546232 (Marketing)
Fax: 0937 546333

Services offered include: loans, urgent action service, Lexicon easy order service, copyright clearance, journals contents page, tailor made services.

BMA Library
Tavistock Square
London WC1H 9JP

Tel: General/Loan enquiries: 071 383 6625
   Reference enquiries: 071 383 6060
Fax: 071 388 2544

Holdings: 38,000 books (2,000 new titles a year); 3,000 periodicals (1,200 current subscriptions – reprinted catalogue available free of charge); largest collection of medical films and videos in the UK – includes over 1,000 contemporary VHS cassettes.

178

Information held in stock: clinical medicine/social & political aspects of medicine/medical ethics.

Computer retrieval: see below.

Services offered include: photocopying by mail, fax, EMAIL, or in person. Urgent requests can be faxed or sent within a few hours of receiving the request. Literature searching, video previewing/loans, book loans, C-D ROMS including MEDLINE, library aids and BMJ databases, Enquiry pass on.

Council of International Hospitals/Advisory Board Company
The Watergate
600 New Hampshire Avenue, NW
Washington DC 20037

UK office:
PO Box 4NG
London W1A 4NG

Tel: 202 672 5600 (US). 071 388 8870 (UK)
Fax: 202 672 5600 (US). 071 388 8817 (UK)

Holdings: c6,000 custom research projects.

Services offered include: custom research, instant services, fact briefs, issue briefs, custom project library.

Information Resource Centre
Nuffield Institute for Health
71–75 Clarendon Road
Leeds LS2 9PL

Tel: 0532 459034
Fax: 0532 460899

Holdings: 30,000 books, 300 journals, 270 current titles.

Information held in stock: health administration/social care/demography/ epidemiology/public health/economics/management/marketing/organisational psychology/statistics/quality/benchmarking/quality/performance indicators.

All the above in relation to non-clinical health and social care management.

Special Strengths: Community care/health outcomes.

Computer retrieval: DATASTAR/BLAISE/DIALOG/ESA/IRS (online). HELMIS (Health Management Information Service) – compiled in-house and available via PDN.

Services offered include: HELMIS ONLINE, a constantly updated database currently containing some 40,000 records relating to health and social care management, literature searches, monthly *Health Management Update*, bi-monthly *Community Care Update*, document delivery.

International Benchmarking Clearing House
American Productivity & Quality Center
123 North Post Oak Lane
Houston
Texas, TX77024-7797

Tel: (713) 685-4666
Fax: (713) 681-5321

Management Information Centre
Institute of Management
Management House
Cottingham Road
Corby
Northants

Tel: 0536 204222
Fax: 0536 201651

Information held in stock: management/marketing/quality/health/informatics/
benchmarking/performance indicators.

Computer retrieval: various/comprehensive.

Services offered include: an enquiry service covering a) reading lists,
b) tailored searches, c) book loans, d) provision of photocopies, e) factsheets,
f) specialised research, g) online search service; 2. International Databases
Plus produced in conjunction with Bowker-Saur and 3. Management
Information Databases (+ Management Helpline). Courses available.

King's Fund Centre
126 Albert Street
London NW1 7NF

Tel: 071 267 6111
Fax: 071 267 6108

For Health Service only—Holdings: 26,000 books, 430 journals.

Information held in stock: management/quality/health/informatics/
comparative information/performance indicators/health administration.

Special collections: WHO Regional Office for Europe, Medical Audit Information Service Collection, Health and Race Publications, DOH Circulars.

Computer retrieval: DATASTAR, BLAISE, DIALOG, (online – charged
computer time only).

Services offered include: 1. Unicorn Database, 2. Online Commercial
Databases, 3. Photocopies, 4. World Health Organisation Regional Office for
Europe – Official Documentation Centre, 5. Medical Audit Information
Service, 6. Nursing Audit Information Service.

Medical Information Centre
The British Library
Boston Spa
Wetherby
West Yorkshire LS23 7BQ

Tel: 0937 546364
Fax: CCITT Group III 0937 546039

Services offered include: 1. BLAISE – LINK through a partnership with US National Library of Medicine, 2. Computer databases searches.

Office of Population Census and Surveys
St Catherines House
10 Kingsway
London WC2B 6JP

Tel: 071 396 2236
Fax: 071 430 1779

Holdings: 50,000 books, 400 journals, 350 current titles, 300 microfilms.

Information held in stock: statistics/government/management/quality/ informatics/health/medical/comparative information.

Special collections: Census Data/Foreign Censuses

Computer retrieval: DATASTAR, DIALOG (online), MEDLINE, 1981 Small Area Statistics Census (CD-ROM).

Services offered include: photocopies/offprints, accessions list, bibliographies.

Pira International
Randalls Road
Leatherhead
Surrey KT22 7RU

Tel: 0372 376161
Fax: 0372 360104

Services offered include: publishing of abstracts journals including *Management & Marketing Abstracts.*

Royal College of General Practitioners
14 Princes Gate
Hyde Park
London SW7 1PU

Tel: 071 581 3232
Fax: 071 225 3047

For GPs only—Holdings: 3,500 books, 234 journals (192 current titles), 80 practice annual reports, 250 practice premises plans, 300 practice information leaflets, 100 specimens of patient record cards.

Special collection: general practice.

Information held in stock: medical.

Computer retrieval: DATASTAR, BLAISE, DIALOG, PROFILE (all online – standard charge).

Services offered include: Literature searching.

SilverPlatter Information Ltd
10 Barley Mow Passage
Chiswick
London W4 4PH

Tel: 081 995 8242
Tel: 0800 262 096
Fax: 081 995 5159

Services offered: suppliers of CD-ROMS including 1. HealthPLAN CD, 2. MEDLINE STANDARD, 3. Nursing & Allied Health (CINAHL)-CD, AIDSLINE, biological abstracts, cancer-CD, international pharmaceutical abstracts, MDX health digest, Meyler's side effects of drugs database, MEDLINE professional, MEDLINE express, POPLINE, anaesthesiology, cardiology, drugs & pharmocology, gastroentorology, immunology & AIDS, nephrology, nuerosciences, obstetrics & gynaecology, pathology, psychiatry, radiology and nuclear medicine, The Excerpta Medica Library Service. Also tailor made CD-Rom packages available.

More Information

NHS Benchmarking Award

Benchmarking for Healthy Services

Introduction

The NHS Benchmarking Reference Centre is pleased to launch the NHS Benchmarking Award to recognise achievements in benchmarking.

The purpose of the award is to promote excellence through benchmarking by recognising the benchmarking contributions of individuals and teams.

The award is administered by the NHS Benchmarking Reference Centre. Applications will be evaluated by an independent panel of experts who have considerable experience of benchmarking.

The panel of judges provides senior management oversight, assures the objectivity of the award process, and improves the definition and applicability of the award criteria. Judges will be appointed by the Award administrator.

In 1994/5 the Award was a travel scholarship worth up to £2500 sponsored by SmithKline Beecham. In 1995/6 it is planned to extend the award to all public sector organisations.

Who Can Apply?

The NHS Benchmarking Award scheme is open to all health-care organisations who have adopted benchmarking as a tool for continous improvement in the commissioning, provision and support of delivery of health-care and who are successfully utilising the benchmarking approach.

Why Apply?

- To encourage excellence/best practice benchmarking through recognition of individuals and teams.
- For self-assessment and feedback.
- To become a model of excellence/best practice in benchmarking.
- To raise standards for achievement in process and results.
- Focuses on the approach and deployment of benchmarking, as well as results from the benchmarking studies.

Further details are available from The Award Administration at The NHS Benchmarking Reference Centre (see below).

Benchmarking Briefing

Benchmarking Briefing is a newsletter published by Longman Health Management in association with the NHS Benchmarking Reference Centre. Use it to locate benchmarking initiatives in the health service throughout the UK.

Practical and focused to aid self-help, this newsletter will enable you to achieve a competitive edge using tried and tested techniques, maintain a leading position in health service delivery, and combine clinical and managerial aims and objectives to achieve excellence. Whether you are a trust, a trust-in-waiting, a health authority or a GP fundholder, you will find something of value in *Benchmarking Briefing*.

NHS Benchmarking Reference Centre

The Reference Centre was launched in September 1992, and was established to promote, facilitate and improve benchmarking by helping organisations in the NHS improve quality and performance through learning from best practices.

Since it was established the Reference Centre has played a key role in developing and implementing benchmarking with the service.

An awareness programme has been established, using management presentations, seminars, conferences and training days.

A national comparative database for hospitals has been established, and the Centre has facilitated a number of benchmarking projects with acute and community units.

New projects are being developed with commissioning authorities, ambulance services, hotel services and scientific services.

The Centre has also facilitated the development of a number of Benchmarking Clubs and networks, and is a member of the Steering Group of the all-industry Benchmarking Centre Ltd.

The Reference Centre has links with many organisations both at a national and international level including other NHS organisations, the Audit Commission, business and industry, research institutions, and management consultants.

Benchmarking is gaining wide recognition as one of the most powerful and useful ways to improve performance and quality in all organisations.

However, benchmarking is not always easy. Most organisations need training in the process and guidance about where to go, what to ask, and what to do with the information obtained.

The Reference Centre can offer a range of services which will help you organise and manage the process. These services have been designed to support every stage of benchmarking, to ensure that benchmarking results in continuous improvement. Services offered by the Reference Centre include:

Information Service

The Reference Centre has a growing network of information on processes and best practices. In addition, it has access to International Clearing Houses who are also able to provide information on benchmarking and best practices in the United States and Europe.

The Centre also maintains an up-to-date 'resource bank' of support materials for benchmarking, including articles, books, bibliographies, conference proceedings, training, materials, videos and case studies.

Networking Services

The key to knowing who is best and how to contact them is one of the most challenging parts of benchmarking. The Reference Centre solves this problem in a number of ways:

- member contact lists;
- benchmarking database;
- Code of Conduct;
- new Benchmarking Clubs.

The Centre can offer a number of benchmarking services including details of benchmarking studies, benchmarking initiative schemes and the Code of Conduct which promotes the highest standards in every interaction with the Reference Centre.

Training and Conferences

The Reference Centre has a benchmarking training package which has been designed to suit local needs.

The Centre also organises benchmarking conferences and seminars both at a local and national level.

Literature and Publications

A large selection of up-to-date literature is available from the Reference Centre. It includes articles on benchmarking, journals, books, videos, training materials, conference materials, good practice guides, the *Benchmarking Newsletter* and the *Benchmarking Code of Conduct*. This is a set of guidelines that we encourage all organisations and individuals involved in benchmarking to abide by. The Code of Conduct encourages the principles of sharing best practice and information exchange.

Even if your organisation is not yet benchmarking, the services offered by the Reference Centre can help you get started, help managers and staff understand and improve their processes, get new ideas and find the training they need.

To Join the NHS Benchmarking Reference Centre ...

The annual subscription of £1950 will give your organisation access to all the services listed. One year's membership will entitle you to:

- 1 day's consultancy/training (by VFM staff) to help your organisation with benchmarking, eg training in benchmarking techniques, process mapping.
- 1 set of all benchmarking publications (produced by the NHS Benchmarking Reference Centre). NB 1 set = a copy of existing guide and the *Benchmarking Briefing* newsletter.
- 2 tickets for the annual NHS National NHS Benchmarking Conference.
- Access to the Reference Centre's library and search facilities ('gateway' to national and international databases).
- Access to value added services, eg WHICH database, High Level Indicators (these services will be provided by VFM at preferential rates).
- Opportunity to join appropriate Benchmarking Clubs and support networks.

The NHS Benchmarking Reference Centre offers the opportunity for organisations to pursue benchmarking, to learn what makes organisations the 'best of the best' and to put that learning into practice.

If you would like to receive further details or join the NHS Benchmarking Reference Centre, please contact:

Dr John Bullivant
Executive Director
NHS Benchmarking Reference Centre
VFM Unit
Croesnewydd Hall
Wrexham Technology Park
Wrexham
Clwyd LL13 7YP

Tel: 0978 316230
Fax: 0978 316231

Other organisations

CHKS Ltd
National Comparative Database Service
1 Arden Court
Arden Road
Alcester
Warks B49 6HN

Tel: 0789 765555
Fax: 0789 764608

DataTree Software Ltd
Kinmel Manor
81 Georges Road
Abergele
Clwyd LL22 9AS

Tel: 0745 822220
Fax: 0745 822230

Joint Commission on Accreditation of Healthcare Organisations (JCAHO)
One Renaissance Boulevard
Oakbrook terrace
Illinois 60181
USA

Tel: (708) 916-5600

Chartered Institute of Management Accountants (CIMA)
63 Portland Place
London W1N 4AB

Tel: 071 637 2311
Fax: 071 631 5309

Chartered Institute of Public Finance and Accountants (CIPFA)
3 Roberts Street
London WC2N 6BH

Tel: 071 895 8823
Fax: 071 895 8825

The Audit Commission for Local Authorities and the NHS in England and Wales
1 Vincent Square
London SW1P 2PN

Tel: 071 828 1212
Fax: 071 976 6187

Index